Fiona Mapp

ESSENTIALS

Year 8
KS3 Mathematics
Coursebook

How to Use this Coursebook

A Note to the Teacher

This coursebook includes coverage of the Level 1 Functional Skills for Maths appropriate to Year 8. Guidance and practice material relating to these skills is integrated into the main content of the book to reflect the structure of the new Programme of Study.

Each coursebook comprises...
- clear, concise content appropriate to that year
- questions and tasks to reinforce students' learning and help improve their confidence.

Where appropriate, the coursebooks relate mathematical concepts to real-life situations, to illustrate the importance of maths beyond the classroom.

This Year 8 coursebook is split into 16 topics. Each topic has the following features:
- **Content** that students need to learn.

- **Key words** picked out in colour in the text and listed at the end of the section.
- A **Quick Test** to assess students' understanding through a combination of theory-based questions, multiple choice questions and true / false questions.
- **Skills Practice** questions to provide students with the opportunity to practise what they have learned.

Selected topics have an **extension / activity** to further reinforce students' understanding. These take the form of a practical activity or investigation.

Also included in the centre of the book is a pull-out answer booklet. It contains the answers to all of the questions in this coursebook.

Each coursebook is supported by a workbook to provide further practice and help consolidate learning.

A Note to the Student

We're sure you'll enjoy using this coursebook, but follow these helpful hints to make the most of it:
- Try to write answers that require reasoning or explanation in good English, using correct punctuation and good sentence construction. Read what you have written to make sure it makes sense.
- Think carefully when drawing graphs. Always make sure that you have labelled your axes, given your graph a title and plotted points accurately.
- Try to learn what all the key words mean.

- Where questions require you to make calculations, remember to show your workings. In tests, you might get marks for a correct method even if you arrive at the wrong answer.
- The tick boxes on the Contents page let you track your progress: simply put a tick in the box next to each topic when you're confident that you know it.

You might need a calculator to answer questions that carry this symbol. All other questions should be attempted without using a calculator and you should show your workings.

Contents

Numbers

Multiplying a 3-Digit Number By a 2-Digit Number

There are two different methods that can be used.

Method 1: Grid Method

524×63

×	500	20	4
60	30 000	1200	240
3	1500	60	12

31 440 ⟵ 30 000 + 1200 + 240
1 572+ ⟵ 1500 + 60 + 12
33 012

Method 2: Long Multiplication

$$
\begin{array}{r}
5\ 2\ 4 \\
6\ 3\ \times \\
\hline
1\ 5\ 7_1\ 2 \\
3\ 1_1\ 4_2\ 4\ 0 \\
\hline
3\ 3\ 0\ 1\ 2 \\
\small 1\ 1
\end{array}
$$

1 5 7₁ 2 ⟵ 524 × 3
3 1₁ 4₂ 4 0 ⟵ 524 × 60

Either method can be used but be careful when carrying numbers.

Dividing a 3-Digit Number By a 2-Digit Number

Example
Divide 882 by 49

Method 1

$$
\begin{array}{r}
18 \\
49\overline{)882} \\
49 \\
\hline
392 \\
392 \\
\hline
0
\end{array}
$$

Step 1: 49 goes into 88 once
Step 2: Subtract 49 from 88
Step 3: Bring down the 2
Step 4: 49 goes into 392 8 times, with no remainder

Method 2

$$
\begin{array}{r}
18 \\
49\overline{)882} \\
490 \\
\hline
392 \\
245 \\
\hline
147
\end{array}
$$

Step 1: 490 (10 × 49) is less than 882, so 49 goes into 882 at least ⑩ times
Step 2: Subtract 490 from 882
Step 3: 5 × 49 = 245, so 49 goes into 392, ⑤ times
Step 4: Subtract 245 from 392 (= 147)
Step 5: ③ × 49 = 147
Step 6: Add the 10, 5 and 3 together, so 49 goes into 882 18 times

Indices

An **index** is sometimes known as a **power**.

Examples
7^5 is read as '7 to the power of 5'.
This means $7 \times 7 \times 7 \times 7 \times 7$
4^9 is read as '4 to the power of 9'.
This means $4 \times 4 \times 4 \times 4 \times 4 \times 4 \times 4 \times 4 \times 4$

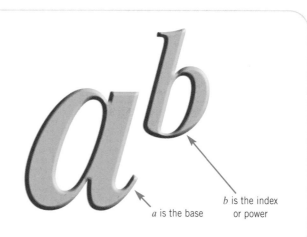

b is the index or power
a is the base

BIDMAS

BIDMAS helps you to remember the order for calculations.

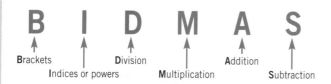

B Brackets
I Indices or powers
D Division
M Multiplication
A Addition
S Subtraction

The brackets are worked out first, then any powers, then division and multiplication are done before addition and subtraction.

Examples

Work out...

1 $7 \times (5 - 3)$
  $= 7 \times 2$
  $= 14$

2 $(27 - 5^2) \times 2$
  $= (27 - 25) \times 2$
  $= 2 \times 2$
  $= 4$

3 $(15 \times 2) \div (2 \times 3)$
  $= 30 \div 6$
  $= 5$

4 $20 \div (7 - 3)$
  $= 20 \div 4$
  $= 5$

Calculating Powers

y^x or x^y or $x^\blacksquare$ are used for calculating powers such as 5^4.

Bell Punch Co.

At the end of 1961, the Bell Punch Company brought out the 'Anita MKVII' and 'Anita MK 8' as the world's first electronic desktop calculators.

Using a Calculator

It's important that you know how your calculator works.

SHIFT or 2nd or Inv allows second functions to be carried out.

– or (–) changes positive numbers to negative ones.

Example

$5^2 + (2 \times 72) = 169$. Key in:

5 x^2 + (2 × 7 2) =

Square root

Square button

Works out powers

Memory key

Numbers

Types of Numbers

Factors are whole numbers that divide exactly into other whole numbers.

Example
Factors of 20 = 1, 2, 4, 5, 10, 20

Multiples are numbers that are in the multiplication tables.

Example
Six multiples of 10 are 10, 20, 30, 40, 80 and 210.

Prime numbers have only two factors, 1 and itself. The prime numbers up to 20 are 2, 3, 5, 7, 11, 13, 17 and 19.

Square numbers are whole numbers raised to the power of 2. Examples of square numbers are 1, 4, 9, 16, 25, 36, 49, 64, 81 and 100.

Cube numbers are whole numbers raised to the power of 3. Examples of cubed numbers are 1, 8, 27, 64, 125, 216 and 343.

$\sqrt{}$ is the **square root** sign. Taking the square root is the opposite of squaring. $\sqrt{25} = {}^{\pm}5$, since $(5)^2 = 25$ and $(-5)^2 = 25$.

${}^3\sqrt{}$ is the **cube root** sign. Taking the cube root is the opposite of cubing. ${}^3\sqrt{64} = 4$.

> ICT can be used to find an approximate square and cube root by using Excel or a similar spreadsheet package

The **reciprocal** of a number $\frac{a}{x}$ is $\frac{x}{a}$

The reciprocal of $\frac{5}{9}$ is $\frac{9}{5}$

Multiplying a number by its reciprocal always gives 1. Zero has no reciprocal.

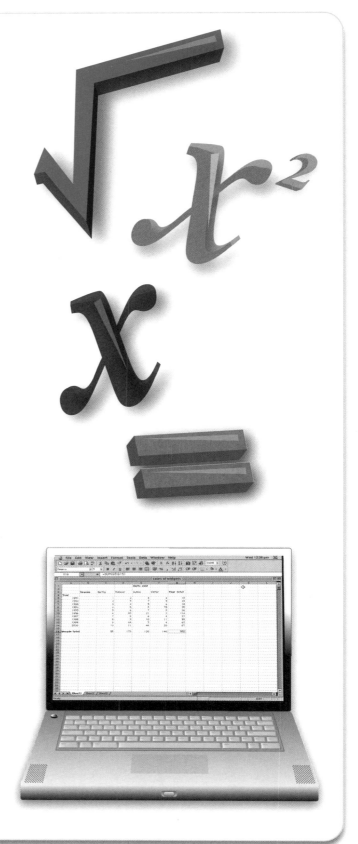

Prime Factors

Prime factors are factors that are prime numbers. Numbers can be written as the **product** of their prime factors. (A product is found by multiplying two or more numbers together.)

Example

The diagram shows prime factors of 30:
- Divide 30 by its first prime factor, 2.
- Divide 15 by its first prime factor, 3.
- Keep on until the final number is prime.

As a product of its prime factors, 30 may be written as: $2 \times 3 \times 5 = 30$

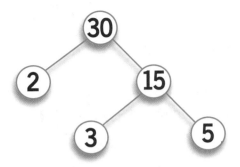

Highest Common Factor

The highest factor that two numbers have in common is called the highest common factor (**HCF**).

Example

Find the HCF of 60 and 84.

Write the numbers as a product of their prime factors:

$60 = 2 \times 2 \times 3 \times 5$
$84 = 2 \times 2 \times 3 \times 7$

> The prime factors of 60 could be written as $2^2 \times 3 \times 5$ in index notation

Now circle the common factors.

These give the HCF as $2 \times 2 \times 3 = 12$

The HCF of 60 and 84 is 12.

Least Common Multiple

The least common multiple (**LCM**) is the lowest number that is a multiple of two or more numbers.

Example

Find the LCM of 12 and 20.

Write the numbers as a product of their prime factors.

$12 = 2 \times 2 \times 3$

$20 = 2 \times 2 \quad \times 5$

Line up the columns carefully. Take one number from each column.

The LCM of 12 and 20 is:
$2 \times 2 \times 3 \times 5 = 60$

Quick Test

1. Work out the answer to 246×83.
2. Work out the answer to $390 \div 26$.
3. $5 \times 5 \times 5 \times 5$ is read as '4 to the power of 5'. True or false?
4. Work out:
   $9^2 - (4^2 + 2^3)$
5. What are the prime factors of 36?
6. Work out the answer to 234×56

KEY WORDS

Make sure you understand these words before moving on!
- Index
- Power
- BIDMAS
- Factor
- Multiple
- Prime number
- Square number
- Cube number
- Square root
- Cube root
- Reciprocals
- Prime factors
- Product
- HCF
- Index notation
- LCM

Numbers

1 362 pupils are going on a trip. A coach can seat 48 people. Work out how many coaches are needed and how many seats are empty in the final coach.

2 A garden centre buys 248 trees costing £68 per tree. How much did they spend?

3 Write the following in index notation:

a) $6 \times 6 \times 6 \times 6 \times 6$

b) $2 \times 2 \times 2 \times 2 \times 2 \times 2$

c) $8 \times 8 \times 8 \times 8$

4 Write the following out fully:

a) 5^9 b) 10^7 c) $2^3 \times 3^5$

5 Work out the following:

a) $5 + (2 \times 6)$

b) $16 - (3^2 + 1)$

c) $5^2 \times (2 \times 3^2)$

d) $81 - 2 \times 7$

e) $(81 - 2) \times 7$

6 Use your calculator to work out the following:

a) $5 + (2 - 9)^2$

b) $6 + (3 \times 2)$

c) $\dfrac{15 + 9}{2 \times 6}$

7 Work out the following:

a) $\sqrt{64}$

b) $\sqrt{81}$

c) $\sqrt{169}$

d) 5^2

e) 4^3

f) $\sqrt[3]{729}$

8 Write the following as a product of prime factors:

a) 25

b) 32

c) 18

d) 100

9 Find the HCF and the LCM of:

a) 42 and 20

b) 16 and 36

10 A gardener buys 174 bags of bulbs at 79p per bag. How much was the total cost of the bulbs?

Fractions, Decimals & Estimating

Fractions – A Quick Reminder

A **fraction** is a whole unit divided into equal parts.

$\dfrac{5}{7}$ ← the **numerator**
  ← the **denominator**

$\dfrac{5}{7}$ is a **proper fraction**.

$\dfrac{7}{5}$ is called an **improper fraction**.

A fraction that has a whole number and a fraction is called a **mixed number**, for example, $5\frac{1}{3}$

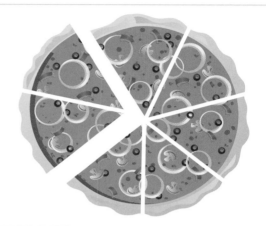

Adding & Subtracting Fractions

Only fractions with the same denominator can be added or subtracted.

Example

① Work out $\frac{3}{5} + \frac{2}{3}$

- Find the lowest common denominator of 5 and 3. In this case it's 15.
- Change the fractions into their equivalent with a denominator of 15.

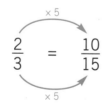

$$\overset{\times 3}{\underset{\times 3}{\frac{3}{5}}} = \frac{9}{15} \qquad \overset{\times 5}{\underset{\times 5}{\frac{2}{3}}} = \frac{10}{15}$$

Now rewrite the sum:

$\frac{9}{15} + \frac{10}{15} = \frac{19}{15} = 1\frac{4}{15}$

② Work out $3\frac{4}{5} - 1\frac{2}{7}$

Rewrite as improper fractions then continue as normal:

$\frac{19}{5} - \frac{9}{7}$

$= \frac{133}{35} - \frac{45}{35}$

$= \frac{88}{35}$

$= 2\frac{18}{35}$

Multiplying & Dividing Fractions

When multiplying and dividing fractions, write whole or mixed numbers as improper fractions.

Example

$\dfrac{5}{7} \times \dfrac{4}{9} = \dfrac{20}{63}$ ← Multiply the numerators together
  ← Multiply the denominators together

For division, turn the second fraction upside down (taking the reciprocal) and multiply the fractions together.

Example

$3\frac{1}{2} \div \frac{4}{5}$

$= \frac{7}{2} \div \frac{4}{5}$

$= \frac{7}{2} \times \frac{5}{4}$ ← Turn the second fraction upside down and multiply with $\frac{7}{2}$

$= \frac{35}{8} = 4\frac{3}{8}$ ← Give the answer as a mixed number

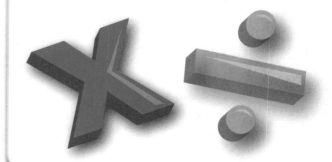

The Fraction Key on the Calculator

⌨ is the fraction key.

Example

$\frac{5}{7}$ is keyed in as [5] [⌨] [7]

This is displayed as ⌐5 ⌐ 7⌐

The calculator will automatically cancel down fractions when the [=] is pressed.

A display of ⌐3 ⌐ 5 ⌐ 9⌐ means $3\frac{5}{9}$

If you press [SHIFT] [⌨] [=] it converts to an improper fraction: $\frac{32}{9}$

Fractions of a Quantity

To find a fraction of a quantity, you multiply the fraction by the quantity.

Example

Out of 6000 people surveyed only $\frac{2}{5}$ of them eat five helpings of fruit or vegetables per day.

$\frac{2}{5}$ of 6000 is:

$\frac{2}{5} \times 6000 = 2400$ people

$6000 \div 5 = 1200$
$1200 \times 2 = 2400$

Egyptian Fractions

The Egyptians of 3000BC had an interesting way to represent fractions. They could write unit fractions like $\frac{1}{2}$, $\frac{1}{4}$ and $\frac{1}{3}$ but they couldn't write fractions like $\frac{2}{3}$ or $\frac{3}{4}$ as we can. Instead they would write any fraction as a sum of unit fractions, where all the unit fractions were different.

Example

$\frac{3}{4} = \frac{1}{2} + \frac{1}{4}$

$\frac{6}{7} = \frac{1}{2} + \frac{1}{3} + \frac{1}{42}$

A fraction written as a sum of distinct unit fractions is called an Egyptian fraction.

Fractions, Decimals & Estimating

Decimals

Decimals are used for parts of numbers that are less than 1. A decimal point is used to separate whole number columns from fractional columns.

72.4 has 7 tens, 2 units and 4 tenths.

A terminating decimal is a decimal that ends, for example 6.42

All terminating decimals can be converted to a fraction using place value:

$0.3 = \frac{3}{10}$ $0.47 = \frac{4}{10} + \frac{7}{100} = \frac{47}{100}$

A recurring decimal is a decimal in which one or more figures repeat.

To show that a figure recurs, place a dot above the figure or figures:

0.3333 is written as $0.\dot{3}$

0.252525 is written as $0.\dot{2}\dot{5}$

0.123412341... is written as $0.\dot{1}23\dot{4}$

Ordering Decimals

When ordering decimals...
1. firstly write them with the same number of digits after the decimal point
2. then compare whole numbers, digits in the tenths place, digits in the hundredths place, and so on.

Example
Arrange these numbers in order of size, smallest first:

5.63, 5.621, 5.029, 5.03, 5.14, 5.137

First rewrite them: 5.630, 5.621, 5.029, 5.030, 5.140, 5.137

Then reorder them: 5.029, 5.030, 5.137, 5.140, 5.621, 5.630

The 2 is worth less than the 3

Multiplying & Dividing Decimals

When multiplying decimals, use the same method as you would use for multiplying ordinary numbers. Then find the position of the decimal point.

Examples

1 4.62×3.5

This requires long multiplication. It is made easier if you multiply 4.62 by 100 and 3.5 by 10 to remove the decimal point.

$$
\begin{array}{r}
4\,62 \\
35\times \\
\hline
2\,3{}_3 1{}_1 0 \\
13{}_1 860+ \\
\hline
16\,170 \\
\end{array}
$$

462×5

462×30

Now divide the answer by 100 and then 10:

$16\,170 \div 100 = 161.70$

$161.70 \div 10 = 16.17$

2 $58.6 \div 0.4$

$58.6 \div 0.4$ is equivalent to $586 \div 4$ (multiplying both numbers by 10).

$$
\begin{array}{r}
146.5 \\
4\,\overline{)\,5^1 8^2 6.^2 0} \\
\end{array}
$$

so $58.6 \div 0.4 = 146.5$

When multiplying by numbers between 0 and 1, the result is smaller than the starting value.

Example

$5 \times 0.1 = 0.5$

$5 \times 0.01 = 0.05$

$5 \times 0.001 = 0.005$

When dividing by numbers between 0 and 1, the result is bigger than the starting value.

Example

$3 \div 0.1 = 30$

$3 \div 0.01 = 300$

$3 \div 0.001 = 3000$

Rounding Decimals

Decimals can be rounded to the nearest whole number or a given number of decimal places. Rounding decimals is useful in calculations and also when measuring.

When rounding to a specified number of decimal places:

1 Look at the digit to the right of the last required place, for example to round to the nearest tenth (one decimal place), look at the number in the second decimal place.

2 If the number that is not needed is 5 or more, round up the last required digit. If it is less than 5 the last required digit remains the same.

Examples

$7.29 = 7.3$ (to 1 d.p.)

$15.235 = 15.24$ (to 2 d.p.)

$6.381 = 6.38$ (to 2 d.p.)

$142.3645 = 142.365$ (to 3 d.p.)

Fractions, Decimals & Estimating

Significant Figures

The first **significant figure** (*sf* or *sig fig*) is the first digit that is not zero. The second, third, fourth... significant figures follow on after the first digit. They may or may not be zeros.

Examples

2.7305 has 5 *sf*

1ˢᵗ 2ⁿᵈ 3ʳᵈ 4ᵗʰ 5ᵗʰ

0.00239 has 3 *sf*

1ˢᵗ 2ⁿᵈ 3ʳᵈ

To round a number to a given number of significant places, apply the same rules as with decimal places. If the next digit is 5 or more, round up.

Number	to 3 *sf*	to 2 *sf*	to 1 *sf*
5.306	5.31	5.3	5
4268	4270	4300	4000
0.720	0.720	0.72	0.7

After rounding the last digit you must fill in the end zeros, for example 275 = 280 to 2 *sf*.

Estimating and Approximates

Estimating is a good way of checking your answer. It is useful when shopping to estimate the cost of your purchases.

When estimating...
- round the numbers to easy numbers, usually ones with 1 or 2 significant figures
- use the symbol ≈ this means 'approximately equal to'
- when multiplying and dividing, don't approximate a number to zero, use 0.1, 0.01, etc.

Examples

£1.49 + £0.49 + £1.09
≈ £1.50 + £0.50 + £1.00 = £3.00

$9.21 \times 10.98 \approx 9 \times 11 = 99$

$0.082 \times 42 \approx 0.1 \times 40 = 4$

$$\frac{398 \times 53.1}{19.6 \times 0.097} \approx \frac{400 \times 50}{20 \times 0.1}$$

$$= \frac{20\,000}{2}$$

$$= 10\,000$$

When adding or subtracting, very small numbers can be approximated to zero.

200.1 + 0.0037
≈ 200 + 0
= 200

Till Receipt

Carrots £1.49
Peas 49p
Milk £1.09

Total: £3.07

Checking Calculations

To check a calculation, the calculation can be reversed.

Example

$526 \times 9 = 4734$

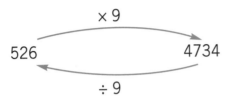

Check with $4734 \div 9 = 526$

$729 + 637 = 1366$

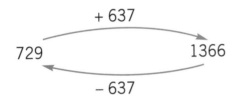

Check with $1366 - 637 = 729$

Quick Test

1. In the number 82.631 what is the place value of the digit 3?

2. Write $\frac{37}{5}$ as a mixed number.

3. What is $2\frac{1}{3} + 1\frac{1}{2}$?

   A $3\frac{2}{5}$ **B** $3\frac{5}{6}$ **C** $3\frac{1}{6}$ **D** $3\frac{2}{3}$

4. The answer to $\frac{4}{7}$ of 21kg is 12kg. True or false?

5. Arrange these numbers in order of size, smallest first:
   3.26, 0.72, 0.719, 3.21, 3.255, 0.76

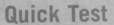

KEY WORDS

Make sure you understand these words before moving on!

- Fraction
- Numerator
- Denominator
- Proper fraction
- Improper fraction
- Mixed number
- Decimal
- Decimal point
- Terminating decimal
- Recurring decimal
- Significant figure
- Estimating

Fractions, Decimals & Estimating

Skills Practice

1 Work out...

a) $\frac{5}{7} + \frac{1}{3}$

b) $\frac{6}{11} - \frac{1}{3}$

c) $\frac{4}{5} - \frac{1}{2}$

d) $\frac{7}{10} + \frac{2}{15}$

e) $2\frac{1}{3} - 1\frac{4}{9}$

f) $5\frac{6}{13} + 2\frac{3}{26}$

2 Work out...

a) $\frac{2}{7} \times \frac{3}{11}$

b) $\frac{5}{9} \times \frac{4}{5}$

c) $\frac{5}{8} \times \frac{1}{2}$

d) $\frac{8}{15} \times \frac{2}{3}$

e) $\frac{4}{7} \times 1\frac{1}{2}$

f) $3\frac{2}{3} \times 1\frac{1}{4}$

3 Work out...

a) $\frac{5}{7} \div \frac{10}{11}$

b) $\frac{6}{11} \div \frac{2}{3}$

c) $\frac{8}{9} \div \frac{3}{5}$

d) $\frac{4}{7} \div \frac{2}{9}$

e) $3\frac{1}{2} \div 2\frac{1}{3}$

f) $5\frac{1}{4} \div 2\frac{1}{8}$

4 Raj earns £35 000 per year. $\frac{2}{5}$ of his salary is used to pay his mortgage. How much does Raj pay towards his mortgage each year?

5 There are 1200 students in a school. $\frac{2}{5}$ of those students eat school lunches. How many eat school lunches?

6 Place each of these sets of decimals in order of size, smallest first:

a) 4.26, 4.31, 4.09, 4.29, 4.293, 4.02

b) 8.73, 8.48, 8.429, 8.475, 8.481, 8.427

c) 6.92, 6.915, 6.902, 6.926, 6.925, 6.931

7 Work out...

a) 41.6×25 **c)** 19.31×4.1 **e)** $98.35 \div 3.5$

b) 27.3×2.8 **d)** $84.76 \div 5.2$ **f)** $82.8 \div 6.9$

8 Round these numbers to two decimal places:

a) 16.425   **c)** 12.869   **e)** 8.712

b) 9.371   **d)** 3.425   **f)** 146.925

9 Round these numbers to the number of significant figures shown in brackets.

a) 572 (2)   **c)** 0.6305 (3)   **e)** 0.027059 (2)

b) 1375 (3)   **d)** 2.7916 (3)   **f)** 15736 (3)

10 Estimate the answers to the following by rounding the numbers to 1 significant figure.

a) 7.6×4.1 **b)** 9.9×3.8 **c)** $(6.1)^2$ **d)** $\dfrac{18.2 \times 41.7}{9.93}$

Negative Numbers

Adding and Subtracting Positive and Negative Numbers

Integers are whole numbers. They can be positive or negative. Positive numbers are above zero and negative numbers are below zero.

Example

The temperature at 2am was -3°C.
By 2pm it had risen 10°C.
What is the new temperature?
-3 + 10 = 7°C

Adding a negative number is the same as subtracting a positive number.
6 + -4 is the same as 6 – 4 = 2

Subtracting a negative number is the same as adding a positive number.
6 – -5 becomes 6 + 5 = 11

Start | Finish

-10 -9 -8 -7 -6 -5 -4 -3 -2 -1 0 1 2 3 4 5 6 7 8 9 10

Multiplying and Dividing Positive and Negative Numbers

When multiplying or dividing two integers you need to check the signs.

Firstly multiply and divide the numbers as normal.

Use these rules to find the sign for the answer:

- Two like signs (both + or -) give a positive result.
- Two unlike signs (one + and the other -) give a negative result.

Examples

$-5 \times (+3) = -15$ $-12 \div (-2) = 6$
$-10 \times (-2) = 20$ $15 \div (-3) = -5$

You should know...

$(+) \times (+) = (+)$ $(+) \div (+) = (+)$

$(-) \times (-) = (+)$ $(-) \div (-) = (+)$

$(+) \times (-) = (-)$ $(+) \div (-) = (-)$

$(-) \times (+) = (-)$ $(-) \div (+) = (-)$

Negative Numbers on the Calculator

The key on the calculator gives a negative number.

For example, to get -5, press (−) 5

This represents the sign

Example

-5 + (-2) = -7

This may be keyed in as follows:

Skills Practice

1 What number is four less than two?

2 Write each set of numbers in order of size, starting with the lowest.
   a) -6, 4, -10, 3, 7, -2, 0, -4, -5
   b) -9, -36, -12, -7, 4, -5, -4, 6
   c) -3, 7, -26, -41, -10, -11, -13, -8

3 Find the value of each of the following:
   a) -6 – 3   **e)** -1 + 10   **i)** 47 – 100
   b) -5 + 2   **f)** 9 – 11   **j)** 5 – 6
   c) 4 – 9   **g)** -65 + 100   **k)** -9 + 10
   d) -6 + 10   **h)** -28 – 10   **l)** 17 – 27

4 Work out...
   a) 5 – -3   **e)** 4 + -3   **i)** -7 – -4
   b) 6 + -2   **f)** -7 – 2   **j)** -6 + -3
   c) -5 + -7   **g)** 6 – -5   **k)** -9 – -2
   d) 2 – -5   **h)** -7 + -2   **l)** 8 + -6

5 Work out...
   a) 7 × -3   **e)** -10 ÷ -2   **i)** 7 × -6
   b) 6 × -2   **f)** -20 ÷ 4   **j)** $(-8)^2$
   c) -5 × -4   **g)** 100 ÷ -2   **k)** 100 ÷ -5
   d) -7 × -3   **h)** -25 ÷ -5   **l)** -50 ÷ -2

6 Use your calculator to work out the following:
   a) -9 + 2 – 6   **e)** -50 ÷ (-2)
   b) -10 – -5 + -3   **f)** -8 – (-2)
   c) 6 – 4 – -7   **g)** 12 + (-6)
   d) -10 × -3 × -2   **h)** -9 × -7 × -1

Percentages

Percentages

A **percentage** is equivalent to a fraction with a denominator of 100, for example $13\% = \dfrac{13}{100}$

Percentages are often seen in everyday life, for example bank interest rates and discounts in summer and winter sales.

Using a Calculator

When finding a percentage of a quantity using a calculator, multiply the quantity by the percentage and divide by 100.

Example
Find 47% of 257m

Key in

`4` `7` `÷` `1` `0` `0` `×` `2` `5` `7` `=`

$\dfrac{47}{100} \times 257m = 120.79m$

Percentages of a Quantity

When finding a percentage of a quantity without a calculator, 10% is the easiest to work out. This is because 10% is the same as one tenth.

Examples
Find:

1 10% of £240

10% is £240 ÷ 10
= £24

2 40% of £60

10% is £60 ÷ 10
= £6
40% is £6 × 4
= £24

Value added tax (VAT) is a tax you pay on the cost of items bought. VAT is generally charged at 20%.

Example
Find the VAT on a jumper that costs £30.

20% = 10% + 10% (or 10% × 2)

10% is £30 ÷ 10
= £3

So VAT charged on a jumper costing £30 is:

£3 + £3 = £6

The actual price of the jumper including VAT is £30 + £6 = £36

© Lonsdale

Increasing and Decreasing by a Percentage

You will often have to find a value when an amount is increased or decreased by a percentage.

Examples

① In a sale, all the prices are reduced by 30%. Find the sale price of a TV which originally cost £699.

Method 1
Work out 30% of £699

$30 \div 100 \times £699 = £209.70$

Subtract this from the original amount
£699 – £209.70 = £489.30

Method 2
Use a **multiplier**. A 30% decrease is a multiplier of 100% – 30% = 70%

70% = 0.7 (just divide 70 by 100)

$£699 \times 0.7 = £489.30$

② The cost of a train ticket increases by 5%. If the original price of the train ticket is £47, using a multiplier method, what is the new cost of the ticket?

An increase of 5% is a multiplier of 100% + 5% = 105%

105% = 1.05 (just divide by 100)

$£47 \times 1.05 = £49.35$

One Quantity as a Percentage of Another

Sometimes you need to write one quantity as a percentage of another.

Example
Write 25cm as a percentage of 3m.

Firstly check that the units are the same, and change if necessary: 3m = 300cm.

Now write as a **fraction**: $\frac{25}{300}$

Now multiply by 100%: $\frac{25}{300} \times 100\% = 8.\dot{3}\%$

Inflation

Inflation is a general rise in prices across the economy. The rate of inflation is given as a percentage. The inflation rate is the measure of the average change in prices across the economy over a specified period – usually 12 months.

This is called the annual rate of inflation.

The target rate of inflation is 2%. But, in June 2008 the inflation rate rose to 3.8%, the highest rate in 16 years. Soaring fuel costs and energy bills were blamed for the rise.

Percentages

Profit and Loss

If you buy a product, the price you pay is the **cost price**. If you sell the product, the price you sell it for is the **selling price**.

Profit (or loss) is the difference between the cost price and the selling price.

You can write profit or loss as the percentage of the original price:

$$\text{Percentage profit (or loss)} = \frac{\text{Profit (or loss)}}{\text{Original amount (or price)}} \times 100\%$$

Examples

1. Charlotte bought a flat for £137 000. She sold it four years later for £185 000. Calculate her percentage profit.

   Profit is £185 000 – £137 000
   $$= £48 000$$
   Percentage profit is $\frac{48\,000}{137\,000} \times 100\% \approx 35\%$

2. Reece bought a new car for £8500. He sold it two years later for £4300. Work out his percentage loss.

   Loss is £8500 – £4300
   $$= £4200$$
   Percentage loss is $\frac{4200}{8500} \times 100\%$
   $$\approx 49\%$$

Repeated Percentage Change

When a quantity is increasing or decreasing over a period of time, we usually use multipliers to work out the percentage change.

Example
A boat was bought for £13 700. During the first year it depreciated in value by 15%, the second year by 10% and the third year by 8%. Work out the value of the boat at the end of the third year.

A decrease of 15% is a multiplier of 0.85
A decrease of 10% is a multiplier of 0.9
A decrease of 8% is a multiplier of 0.92

Value of the boat is 13 700 × 0.85 × 0.9 × 0.92

                                 Year 1 Year 2 Year 3

$$= £9642.06$$

Fractions, Decimals & Percentages

Fractions, **decimals** and percentages are all related:

> Divide the **numerator** by the **denominator** to change to a decimal

$$\frac{1}{2} = 0.5$$

> Multiply the decimal by 100% to change to a percentage

$$0.5 \times 100\% = 50\%$$

The table shows some of the common fractions and their equivalents that you need to learn:

Fraction	Decimal	Percentage
$\frac{1}{2}$	0.5	50%
$\frac{1}{3}$	$0.\dot{3}$	$33.\dot{3}\%$
$\frac{2}{3}$	$0.\dot{6}$	$66.\dot{6}\%$
$\frac{1}{4}$	0.25	25%
$\frac{3}{4}$	0.75	75%
$\frac{1}{5}$	0.2	20%
$\frac{1}{8}$	0.125	12.5%
$\frac{3}{8}$	0.375	37.5%
$\frac{1}{10}$	0.1	10%
$\frac{1}{100}$	0.01	1%

(In the $\frac{3}{4}$ row: $3 \div 4 \rightarrow 0.75 \xrightarrow{\times 100\%} 75\%$)

The Daily News

BANK OF ENGLAND CUTS BASE RATE BY HALF A PERCENT

In October 2008, when the global financial markets were in freefall, the Bank of England and other European banks cut their base rates by 0.5 percent in order to kick start the economy and avoid an economic downturn.

Percentages

Ordering Different Numbers

When putting fractions, decimals and percentages into order of size, it is best to change them all to decimals first.

Example

Place these numbers in order of size, smallest first...

$\frac{1}{3}$, 0.362, 34%, 29.1%, $\frac{2}{9}$, 0.271

Put into decimals:

$0.\dot{3}$, 0.362, 0.34, 0.291, $0.\dot{2}$, 0.271

Now order:

$0.\dot{2}$, 0.271, 0.291, $0.\dot{3}$, 0.34, 0.362

Rewrite in their original form:

$\frac{2}{9}$, 0.271, 29.1%, $\frac{1}{3}$, 34%, 0.362

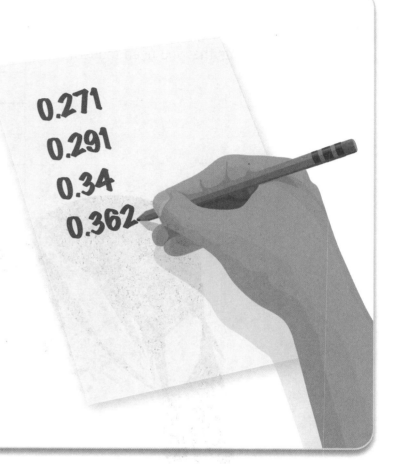

Quick Test

1. Explain how you would find 5% of a quantity.
2. What is 60% of £80?
   A £8 **B** £32 **C** £4.80 **D** £48
3. An increase of 20% is the same as which multiplier?
   A 0.2 **B** 1.2 **C** 0.8 **D** 1.8
4. Write 62kg as a percentage of 80kg.
5. A laptop computer costs £450. It is sold two years later for £320. The percentage loss is 41%. True or false?

Skills Practice

1 There are 140 people on a train. 25% have a newspaper.
How many of them have a newspaper?

2 Use a calculator to find:
a) 12% of 420 miles **b)** 76% of £640 **c)** 37% of 8200g **d)** 28% of 92cm

3 Sarah earns £328 per week. She is given a 3% pay rise.
Work out Sarah's new weekly wage.

4 Write 62kg as a percentage of 125kg.

5 Molly got 16 out of 30 in a Science test. What percentage did she get in the Science test?

6 There are 156 students in Year 11. 63 students study Geography.
What percentage of students study Geography? Give your answer to 1 decimal place.

7 For each of the following, work out the percentage profit:

Garden furniture	Bought: £199	Sold: £320
Bay tree	Bought: £24	Sold: £40
Plant pot	Bought: £9	Sold: £34

8 A lorry was bought for £9500. A year later it was sold for £7100.
Work out the percentage loss.

9 A block of company shares was bought for £200 000. During the first year the value increased by 8% and then in the second year by 4%. What is the value of the block of shares after two years?

10 Place in order of size, smallest first:

41%, $\frac{2}{5}$, 0.369, 37%, $\frac{2}{3}$, 0.409

11 A new games console costs £180.
In a sale it is reduced by 8%.
How much does it now cost?

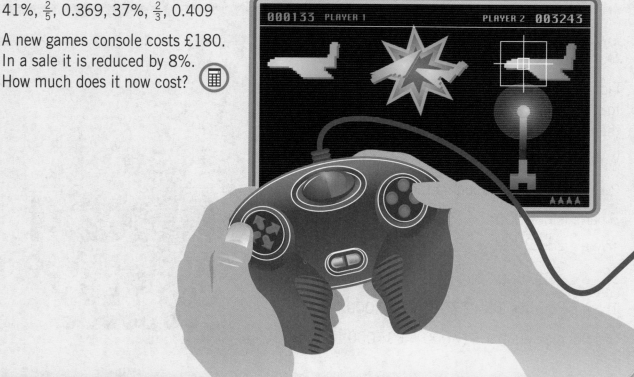

Ratio

What is a Ratio?

A ratio is used to compare two or more quantities. The symbol for ratio is two dots (:).

For example, 12 red apples compared to 20 green apples is written as 12 : 20.

To put ratios in their simplest form, divide both parts of the ratio by the highest common factor.

For example 12 : 20 (divide both parts by 4)
$$= 3 : 5$$

To express the ratio 3 : 5 in the ratio 1 : n, divide both sides by 3

$$3 : 5$$
$$= \frac{3}{3} : \frac{5}{3}$$
$$= 1 : 1\frac{2}{3}$$
Or $1 : 1.\dot{6}$

Using Ratios as Scales

Scale diagrams are often used in building plans and maps to represent distance on the ground. Each length in the scale diagram represents a real length in the building or map.

On the diagram of the car above 2cm represents 1m.

A distance of 8cm on the diagram represents 4m. A distance of 3m in real life would be 6cm on the diagram.

Sharing a Quantity in a Given Ratio

Fiona won £85 000 in the lottery and decided to share it between Samuel and Thomas in the ratio 2 : 3.

Work out how much Thomas and Samuel receive:

$2 + 3 = 5$ parts   (add up the parts)

5 parts is £85 000

1 part is $\frac{£85\,000}{5}$
$$= £17\,000$$

Thomas receives $3 \times £17\,000 = £51\,000$

Samuel receives $2 \times £17\,000 = £34\,000$

Calculating with Ratio

When solving ratio problems remember to reduce one of the ratios to one.

Examples

1 40 maths books cost £760. Work out the cost of buying 27 maths books.

40 books cost   £760

1 book costs $\dfrac{£760}{40}$

= £19

27 books cost 27 × £19

= £513

2 At a bank, Rashna changes £80 into $156.80. How many dollars would Rashna get for changing £230?

£80 is $156.80

£1 is $\dfrac{\$156.80}{80}$

= $1.96

£230 is 230 × $1.96

= $450.80

3 This is a recipe for 8 biscuits:

80g of butter
100g of sugar
2 eggs
120g of flour

How much flour is needed for 12 biscuits?

8 biscuits need   120g of flour

1 biscuit needs $\dfrac{120g}{8}$ = 15g

12 biscuits need 12 × 15g

= 180g

4 It takes 8 builders 6 days to build a playground. At the same rate how long would it take 3 builders?

8 builders take   6 days
1 builder takes   8 × 6 days

= 48 days
3 builders take   48 days ÷ 3

= 16 days

> 3 builders will take a third of the time taken by 1 person

The Golden Ratio

The Golden Ratio is a measurement of about 1.618. The painter Leonardo da Vinci used this to explore the human body, involving the ratio of lengths of various body parts. He called this ratio the 'divine proportion' and featured it in many of his paintings.

Ratio

Best Buys

Many products are sold in different sized boxes. For example, a supermarket may have different sized boxes of cornflakes. It's important to be able to work out which is the best value for money.

500g is £1.69	1g costs 169p ÷ 500 = 0.338p
750g is £2.13	1g costs 213p ÷ 750 = 0.284p
1kg is £2.59	1g costs 259p ÷ 1000 = 0.259p

Example

The same brand of cornflakes is sold in three different sized packets. Which packet represents the best value for money?

Since the 1kg packet costs less per gram it is the best value for money.

(An alternative method for this example would be to work out the cost of 250g.)

500g

£1.69

750g

£2.13

1kg

£2.59

Quick Test

1. The ratio 15 : 30 fully simplified is 2 : 1. True or false?
2. What is the ratio 16 : 24 fully simplified?
   A 8 : 12   **B** 16 : 24   **C** 2 : 3   **D** 3 : 2
3. £36 000 is divided in the ratio 1 : 5. Work out the size of the larger share.
4. 5 pens cost £1.40. How much do 7 pens cost?
5. The ratio 7 : 2 expressed in the form $n : 1$ is 3.5 : 1. True or false?

KEY WORDS

Make sure you understand these words before moving on!
- Ratio
- Simplest form

Skills Practice

1. Write each ratio in its simplest form:
   - **a)** 12 : 15
   - **c)** 6 : 2
   - **e)** 250 : 450
   - **b)** 25 : 50
   - **d)** 12 : 28
   - **f)** 125 : 75

2. In a car park there are 50 silver cars, 36 blue cars and 20 black cars. Write down the ratio of the number of silver cars to black cars to blue cars.

3. In a class, the ratio of left-handed students to right-handed students is 1 : 6. What fraction of the class are left handed?

4. The scale of a map is 1:100 000. Work out the real distance that 7.2cm on the map represents.

5. The ratio of the number of yellow beads to the number of blue beads in a bag is 1 : 4. Work out the number of blue beads if there are 8 yellow beads.

6. £45 is shared in the ratio of 2 : 7. Work out the size of the largest share.

7. William and Edward share 28 marbles in the ratio 2 : 5. Work out how many marbles Edward gets.

8. Ian went on holiday to Spain. The exchange rate was £1 = €1.58 ▦
   He changed £250 into Euros.
   a) Work out the amount of Euros that Ian got.
   When Ian came home he had €88 left. The new exchange rate was £1 = €1.60
   b) Work out how much Ian got in Pounds Sterling for his €88.

9. Here is a list of ingredients to make potato soup for four people: ▦
   200g potatoes, 2 onions, 40g butter and 200ml stock
   Work out how much stock is needed to make potato soup for 14 people.

Number Patterns and Sequences

Number Patterns

A **number pattern** is a list or series of numbers connected by a rule.

Another name for a number pattern is a **sequence**. Each value in the list of numbers is called a **term**.

Example

$$3, \quad 6, \quad 9, \quad 12,...$$
$$+3 \quad +3 \quad +3$$

The rule for this pattern is to add 3 each time. This is called a term-to-term rule

Number patterns can easily be generated by using a spreadsheet.

Number Machines

Number machines can be used to make number patterns. When a sequence of numbers is put into a number machine, the output numbers make a number pattern.

Input			Output
3	× 2	+ 1	7

KEY WORDS
Make sure you understand these words before moving on!
- Number Pattern
- Sequence
- Term
- Common difference

The nth Term

You can find a term in a sequence using a position-to-term rule, if you know the term's position.

Position in Sequence	1	2	3	4	5	n
Term	3	6	9	12	15	$3n$

×3

+3 +3 +3 +3

The term-to-term rule is 'add 3'.

The position-to-term rule is 'multiply by 3'.

The 20th term would be $20 \times 3 = 60$.

The nth term of a sequence is the same as the position-to-term rule, written using algebra.

In the example above, the position-to-term rule is 'multiply by 3'. The nth term would be $3n$.

Example

Position in Sequence	1	2	3	4	5	...	n
Term	7	11	15	19	23	...	$4n+3$

×4
+3

To find the nth term look at the **common difference** between the terms (the term-to-term rule). In this example it is 'add 4'. Since the gap is the same this always multiplies with the nth term, so $4n$.

If you now check: when $n = 1$, $4 \times 1 = 4$. Since the term is 7 we adjust it by adding 3, which gives $4n + 3$.

When $n = 2$, $4 \times 2 + 3 = 11$

So here the nth term is $4n + 3$

Skills Practice

1 For each sequence, write down:
- **i)** the next two numbers
- **ii)** the rule for finding the next number

a) 3, 5, 7, 9,...   **c)** 10, 20, 30, 40,...   **e)** 3, 6, 12, 24,...
b) 10, 8, 6, 4,...   **d)** 100, 50, 25, 12.5,...   **f)** 20, 17, 14, 11,...

2 Look at the sequence of shapes made up of matchsticks.

a) Draw the next two shapes in the sequence.
b) Copy and complete the following table:

Shape	1	2	3	4	5
Number of Matchsticks					

c) How many squares will there be in shape 8?
d) Write down the nth term of this sequence.

3 Find the nth term of each of these sequences:
a) 2, 4, 6, 8, 10,...   **c)** 8, 10, 12, 14, 16,...   **e)** 8, 12, 16, 20, 24,..
b) 3, 5, 7, 9, 11,...   **d)** 5, 7, 9, 11, 13,...

4 For each of the number machines below:
- **i)** input the number pattern 3, 5, 7...
- **ii)** list the output numbers.
- **iii)** describe the pattern it produces.

a)   × 4

b)   × 2   – 1

c)   × 3   + 4

d)   × 5   – 3

Working with Algebra

Algebra

Algebra uses letters to represent values.

Algebra is used to solve many problems.

Definitions Used in Algebra

An **expression** is any arrangement of letters and symbols, e.g. $2z + 3b - 6$.

A **formula** connects two expressions containing variables. The value of one variable depends on the value of another. A formula must have an equals sign. For example:

$F = ma$ is a formula. When the values of m and a are known the value of F can be found.

An **equation** connects two expressions involving definite unknown values. An equation must have an equals sign, e.g. $2x + 1 = 5$.

An **identity** connects expressions involving unspecified numbers. An identity is always true no matter what numerical values replace the letter symbols. It has an $\equiv$ sign, e.g. $4(x - 1) \equiv 4x - 4$.

A **function** is a relationship between two sets of values, so that a value from the first set maps onto a unique value in the second set, e.g. $y = 5x - 1$. For any value of x the value of y can be calculated.

Using Letter Symbols

There are several rules to follow when writing expressions:

$b + b$ is written as $2b$
$b \times c$ is written as bc
$2 \times b \times c$ is written as $2bc$ ← Here the number is written first and the letters put in alphabetical order
$b \times b = b^2$
$b \div 2 = \frac{b}{2}$

Example
In a game, John has x counters. Write down the number of counters each person has using x.
a) Imran has three times as many counters as John. So Imran has $3x$
b) Sophie has ten fewer counters than John so $x - 10$
c) Peta has half as many counters as John so $\frac{x}{2}$
d) Rebecca has four fewer counters than Imran so $3x - 4$

Collecting Like Terms

Expressions can be simplified by collecting like **terms**.

Examples
Simplify...

1 $3a - a = 2a$

2 $2a - b + 6b - 5a = -3a + 5b$ or $5b - 3a$

Add the b's together

Add the a's together

Powers in Algebra

Powers are used in algebra to help write terms in a shorter form.

$a \times a = a^2$

$a \times a \times a = a^3$

$a \times a \times a \times a = a^4$

a^b is read as 'a to the power of b' where a is the base and b is the **power** or **index**.

Examples
1 $2x \times 3x$
$= 2 \times x \times 3 \times x$
$= 6x^2$

2 $3a \times 2b$
$= 3 \times a \times 2 \times b$
$= 6ab$

3 $4x \times 3y \times 2x$
$= 4 \times x \times 3 \times y \times 2 \times x$
$= 24x^2 y$

4 $12a \times 3a \times a$
$= 12 \times a \times 3 \times a \times a$
$= 36a^3$

To multiply powers of numbers or letters add the powers together.

$$y^2 \times y^4 = (y \times y) \times (y \times y \times y \times y)$$
$$= y^6$$
$$y^2 \times y^4 = y^{2+4} = y^6$$

Examples
1 $2a^6 \times a^5 = 2a^{6+5} = 2a^{11}$

2 $2a^5 \times 5a^3 = 10a^8$ ← Add the powers together
Multiply 2 and 5 together

Multiplying Out Single Brackets

Brackets are often used in algebra, for example $3 \times (x - y)$ is usually written as $3(x - y)$.

Multiplying out brackets is often known as 'expanding brackets'. To expand brackets, each term inside the bracket is multiplied by the term outside the bracket.

Examples
Expand...

1 $3(a - b)$
$= 3 \times a - 3 \times b$
$= 3a - 3b$

2 $x(2x - 3y)$
$= x \times 2x - x \times 3y$
$= 2x^2 - 3xy$

3 $5(x - 3) + 2(x - 1)$
$= 5x - 15 + 2x - 2$ ← Multiply out both brackets
$= 7x - 17$ ← Simplify by collecting like terms

4 $3(2x - 1) - 2(x + 1)$
$= 6x - 3 - 2x - 2$
$= 4x - 5$

Working with Algebra

Factorising Simple Expressions

Factorising is the reverse process to that of removing brackets. An expression is put into brackets by taking out **common factors**.

Examples
Factorise...

1 $8x + 12$

$= 4(2x + 3)$

2 $12x - 3y$

$= 3(4x - y)$

3 $20a + 40b$

$= 20(a + 2b)$

4 $5x + x^2$

$= x(5 + x)$ ← *x* is the common factor

Look for the common factors of $8x$ and 12. 4 is the highest common factor, so this can be put outside the bracket. The expression inside the bracket is what is needed so that when multiplied out it returns to the original.

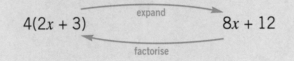

$4(2x + 3)$ →expand→ $8x + 12$

←factorise←

Origins of Algebra

The word 'algebra' comes from the Arabic word *al-jabr*. Al-jabr means 'reunion'. Algebra concerns the study of structure, relation and quantity, and it is one of the main branches of mathematics.

The origins of algebra can be traced to the ancient Babylonians, who developed an advanced arithmetical system which they used to do calculations in an algebraic fashion.

Writing Formulae

A formula can usually be constructed from some information you are given or from a diagram.

Examples

1 Colin buys n bags of sweets at 20p each. He pays with a £5 note. Write down the formula if he receives C pounds change.

$C = 5 - 0.2n$

This is the amount of money he spends per bag. Make sure the units are the same: 20p = £0.20

This represents the amount of money used to buy the sweets

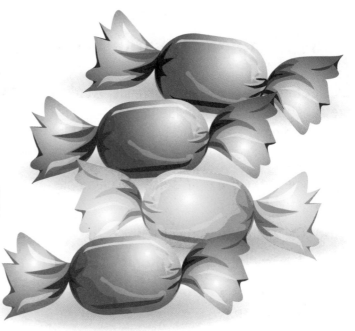

2 Some patterns are made by using grey and white paving slabs.

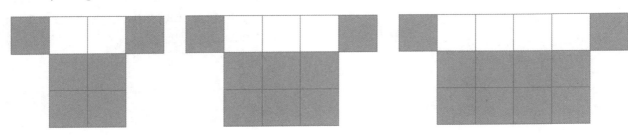

A formula connecting the number of grey paving slabs (g) in a pattern with the number of white (w) ones is:

$g = 2w + 2$

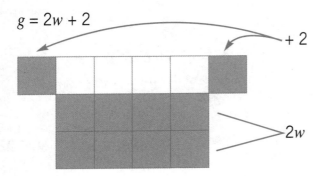

+ 2

$2w$

$2w$ represents the two layers

+ 2 gives the grey slabs on either side.

When there are 20 white slabs there will be $2 \times 20 + 2 = 42$ grey slabs

Working with Algebra

Lots of formulae are used in science. Numbers are substituted into formulae to help solve problems.

Examples

1. In science, $v = u + at$ is used to calculate velocity.

   a) Calculate the value of v if $u = 20$, $a = 12$ and $t = 7$:

   $v = u + at$
   $v = 20 + (12 \times 7)$
   $v = 20 + 84$
   $v = 104$

   b) Calculate the value of v if $u = 15$, $a = -13$ and $t = 6$:

   $v = u + at$
   $v = 15 + (-13 \times 6)$
   $v = 15 - 78$
   $v = -63$

2. If $a = \dfrac{b^2 c}{\sqrt{d}}$

   Find the value of a if $b = 6$, $c = 5.8$ and $d = 49$. Give your answer to 1 decimal place.

   $a = \dfrac{b^2 c}{\sqrt{d}}$

   $a = \dfrac{6^2 \times 5.8}{\sqrt{49}}$

   $a = \dfrac{208.8}{7}$

   $a = 29.8$

   Gas bills are worked out using formulae. The bill depends on how many units of gas have been used.

Quick Test

1. Explain how you should write the term $5 \times b \times d \times a$?
2. What is the expression $3a - 5b + 6b - a$ fully simplified?

   A $4a + 11b$ **C** $4a + 1b$
   B $2a + 2b$ **D** $2a + b$
3. Multiply out the brackets: $3x(x - y)$ gives $3x^2 - 3xy$. True or false?
4. $2a \times 3a \times 2b$ is $8a^2 b$. True or false?
5. $F = ma$. Work out F if $m = 12$ and $a = 3.5$

KEY WORDS

Make sure you understand these words before moving on!

- Algebra
- Expression
- Formula
- Equation
- Identity
- Function
- Term
- Power
- Index
- Factorising
- Common factors

Skills Practice

1 Simplify these expressions by collecting like terms:

a) $3a + 2a - a$

b) $6a - b + 5a$

c) $3x + 10y - 2x - y$

d) $5y - 2y + 10y - y$

e) $5c - 4d - 3d + 6c$

f) $3xy + 2xy - xy^2$

2 Simplify these expressions:

a) $4a \times 2a$

b) $3a \times 6b$

c) $5d \times 3e$

d) $6b \times b$

e) $7a \times 2a$

f) $9p \times 6p$

g) $5a \times 3b \times 2a$

h) $3a \times 2a \times a$

3 Expand and simplify:

a) $5(x - 1)$

b) $3(x + 2y)$

c) $3(2x - 4)$

d) $x(x + 3)$

e) $5(x - 3) + 2(x - 1)$

f) $12(x - 4) - 3(x - 1)$

4 Factorise the following:

a) $15x - 5$

b) $20y + 10$

c) $3x - 9y$

d) $x^2 + 2x$

e) $14y - 2y^2$

f) $9y + 12$

5 If $a = 3$, $b = 4$ and $c = -4$, work out the following expressions:

a) $5a + b$

b) $6a - 2b$

c) $c^2 + 4$

d) $3b - a$

e) $2b^2 + 3$

f) $5b - 2c$

6 In a garden there are x pink flowers. Write down the number of each of the following plants in terms of x.

a) There are three times as many bushes as pink flowers.

b) There are five fewer white flowers than pink flowers.

c) There are half the number of hanging baskets as pink flowers.

Equations and Inequalities

Equations

It was often claimed that the Babylonians (about 400BC) were the first to solve quadratic equations, that is, equations that have an x^2. They developed a method for working out problems that had only positive answers.

An **equation** has two parts separated by an equals sign. When solving an equation, a **solution** to the equation is found. The balance method (doing the same things to both sides of the equation) is often used to find the solution.

Equations of the Form of $ax + b = c$

When solving equations with an unknown on one side, firstly move anything that is added or subtracted to the other side of the equals sign and reverse the operation. You are then left with $ax = d$, which you can **solve**.

Examples

Solve the following:

1
$$7x - 2 = 12$$
$$7x = 12 + 2 \quad \longleftarrow \boxed{\text{Add 2 to both sides}}$$
$$7x = 14$$
$$x = \frac{14}{7} \quad \longleftarrow \boxed{\text{Divide both sides by 7}}$$
$$x = 2$$

2
$$\frac{x}{3} + 4 = 5$$
$$\frac{x}{3} = 5 - 4 \quad \longleftarrow \boxed{\text{Subtract 4 from both sides}}$$
$$\frac{x}{3} = 1$$
$$x = 1 \times 3 \quad \longleftarrow \boxed{\text{Multiply both sides by 3}}$$
$$x = 3$$

Solving Equations of the Form $ax + b = cx + d$

When solving equations with letters on both sides of the equation (in this case x) get all the letters together on one side of the equals sign and the numbers on the other side.

Examples

1
$$3x + 2 = x + 6$$
$$3x + 2 - x = 6 \quad \longleftarrow \boxed{\text{Subtract } x \text{ from both sides}}$$
$$2x = 6 - 2 \quad \longleftarrow \boxed{\text{Subtract 2 from both sides}}$$
$$2x = 4$$
$$x = \frac{4}{2} \quad \longleftarrow \boxed{\text{Divide both sides by 2}}$$
$$x = 2$$

2
$$8x - 10 = 5x + 11$$
$$8x - 10 - 5x = 11 \quad \longleftarrow \boxed{\text{Subtract } 5x \text{ from both sides}}$$
$$8x - 5x = 11 + 10 \quad \longleftarrow \boxed{\text{Add 10 to both sides}}$$
$$3x = 21$$
$$x = \frac{21}{3} \quad \longleftarrow \boxed{\text{Divide both sides by 3}}$$
$$x = 7$$

3
$$10 - 2x = 5x - 4$$
$$10 = 5x - 4 + 2x \quad \longleftarrow \boxed{\text{Add } 2x \text{ to both sides. This will keep the } x\text{'s positive}}$$
$$10 = 7x - 4$$
$$10 + 4 = 7x \quad \longleftarrow \boxed{\text{Add 4 to both sides}}$$
$$14 = 7x$$
$$\frac{14}{7} = x \quad \longleftarrow \boxed{\text{Divide both sides by 7}}$$
$$x = 2$$

Solving Equations with Brackets

When solving equations with brackets always multiply the brackets out first.

Examples

Solve the following:

1 $3(2x + 1) = 15$ ← Multiply out the brackets

$6x + 3 = 15$

$6x = 15 - 3$ ← Subtract 3 from both sides

$6x = 12$

$x = \frac{12}{6}$ ← Divide both sides by 6

$x = 2$

2 $5(3x - 1) = 25$ ← Multiply out the brackets

$15x - 5 = 25$

$15x = 25 + 5$ ← Add 5 to both sides

$15x = 30$

$x = \frac{30}{15}$ ← Divide both sides by 15

$x = 2$

3 $2(x + 3) + 3(x - 1) = 8$ ← Multiply out each bracket

$2x + 6 + 3x - 3 = 8$ ← Collect like terms

$5x + 3 = 8$

$5x = 8 - 3$ ← Subtract 3 from both sides

$5x = 5$

$x = \frac{5}{5}$ ← Divide both sides by 5

$x = 1$

4 $4(2x + 1) = 2(x - 5)$ ← Multiply both sets of brackets out

$8x + 4 = 2x - 10$

$8x + 4 - 2x = -10$ ← Subtract $2x$ from both sides

$6x = -10 - 4$ ← Subtract 4 from both sides

$6x = -14$

$x = -\frac{14}{6}$ ← Divide both sides by 6

$x = -2\frac{1}{3}$

Notice that the answers can be positive or negative, whole or fractional.

Constructing and Solving Linear Equations

When solving problems, a linear equation can be written to find an unknown value.

Examples

1 Use the information in the diagram to...
   a) form an equation
   b) solve the equation to find x.

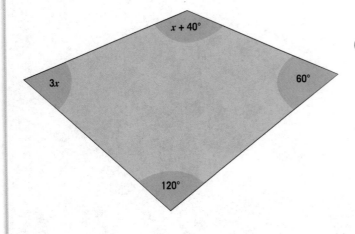

a) $3x + (x + 40°) + 120° + 60° = 360°$

Angles in a quadrilateral add up to 360°

b) $3x + (x + 40°) + 120° + 60° = 360°$

$4x + 220° = 360°$ ← Collect like terms

$4x = 360° - 220°$

$4x = 140°$

$x = \frac{140°}{4}$

$x = 35°$

2 Joshua thinks of a number. He multiplies it by 4 and adds 3. He gets the same answer as if he multiplied his number by 2 and subtracted 1. What number did Joshua think of?

Let's call the number x.

$4x + 3 = 2x - 1$ ← Form the equation

$4x + 3 - 2x = -1$ ← Subtract $2x$ from each side

$4x - 2x = -1 - 3$ ← Subtract 3 from both sides

$2x = -4$

$x = \frac{-4}{2}$

$x = -2$

Equations and Inequalities

Trial and Improvement

With trial and improvement, you try a value in the equation. Keep trying different values, using your previous answer to help you get closer.

Example

The equation $x^2 - x = 15$ has a solution between 4 and 5.

By looking at 4.45 you can see that the true value of x is between 4.4 and 4.45. It is therefore 4.4 to 1 d.p.

ICT can be used to solve an equation by trial and improvement. Set up a spreadsheet to check the solution of the above equation.

Find the solution to one decimal place. Draw a table to help:

x	$x^2 - x = 15$	Comment
4	$4^2 - 4 = 12$	Too small
5	$5^2 - 5 = 20$	Too big
4.5	$4.5^2 - 4.5 = 15.75$	Too big
4.4	$4.4^2 - 4.4 = 14.96$	Too small
4.45	$4.45^2 - 4.4 = 15.35$	Too big

$x^2 - x = 15?$

Inequalities

There are four inequality symbols:

> Means 'greater than'

⩾ Means 'greater than or equal to'

< Means 'less than'

⩽ Means 'less than or equal to'

So, $x > 5$ or $5 < x$ both mean 'x is greater than 5'. $x = 6$ satisfies the inequality $x > 5$.

Example

Put the correct sign between these pairs of numbers:

a) 5 , 9
$5 < 9$
'5 is less than 9'

b) -3 , -5
$-3 > -5$
'-3 is greater than -5'

Inequalities can be represented on a number line:

Use ○ when the end point is not included, e.g. $x < 2$.

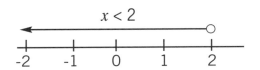

Use ● when the end point is included, e.g. $x \geqslant 5$.

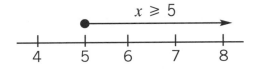

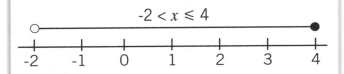

Equations and Inequalities

1. Solve the following:

   a) $x + 2 = 10$

   b) $4x = 16$

   c) $x - 3 = 7$

   d) $2 + x = 10$

   e) $\frac{x}{4} = 2$

   f) $3x = 12$

   g) $\frac{x}{6} = 5$

   h) $x - 2 = 10$

   i) $x + 3 = 4$

   j) $x - 6 = -2$

   k) $3x = -15$

   l) $\frac{x}{5} = -3$

2. Solve the following:

   a) $5x + 1 = 11$

   b) $3x - 2 = 10$

   c) $5 + 4x = 21$

   d) $3x + 5 = 29$

   e) $6x - 1 = 11$

   f) $3x - 5 = 10$

   g) $2x + 1 = 9$

   h) $2x - 6 = 9$

   i) $5x - 1 = 9$

   j) $3x - 6 = 20$

   k) $4x + 3 = 8$

   l) $2x - 3 = 19$

3. Solve the following:

   a) $\frac{3x}{2} + 5 = 7$

   b) $\frac{2x}{5} + 3 = 4$

   c) $\frac{5x}{7} + 3 = 10$

4. Solve the following:

   a) $5x + 2 = 3x + 6$

   b) $3x - 1 = 2x + 8$

   c) $7x + 6 = 2x + 11$

   d) $3x - 2 = x + 4$

   e) $5x - 6 = 3x + 10$

   f) $10 - 7x = 3x + 40$

   g) $6 - 4x = 2x + 24$

   h) $9x - 3 = 4x - 12$

5. Solve the following:

   a) $2(x + 1) = 12$

   b) $3(x - 2) = 21$

   c) $6(x + 1) = 24$

   d) $7(2x - 1) = 35$

   e) $5(x - 3) = 2(x + 6)$

   f) $7(x - 4) = 2(2x + 1)$

   g) $5(2x - 3) = 3(2x - 6)$

   h) $7(x - 1) = 5(x - 3)$

6. Solve $2x^2 + x = 18$ by trial and improvement. Give your answer of the correct solution to 2 decimal places.

7. Put the correct sign between these pairs of numbers to make a true statement:

   a) 5 , 9   b) 7 , 13   c) 15 , 8   d) 9 , 4   e) 7 , 17

8 The perimeter of the rectangle is 40cm.

2x + 5

x + 3

Work out the length and width of the rectangle.

9 Look at the following number pyramid.

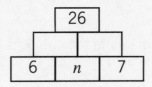

The number in each cell is the sum of the two cells beneath it. Copy and complete the number pyramid and use the information to find *n*.

Graphs

Coordinates

Coordinates are used to locate the position of a point. They are more formally known as Cartesian coordinates and are named after the philosopher Descartes.

Coordinates are used in other subjects, for example, Geography and Science.

Graphs can be used to show the relationship between **variables**.

Rene Descartes
1596 – 1650

Descartes was a French philosopher whose work 'La Geometrie' included his application from algebra to geometry, from which we now have Cartesian Geometry.

Functions and Mapping

Function machines are useful when finding a relationship between two variables.

Example

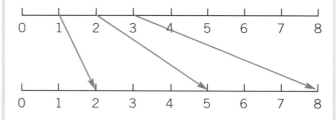

Input (x) → × 3 → -1 → Output (y)

If 1 is fed into the machine, the output is 2 $(1 \times 3 - 1)$.

If 2 is fed into the machine the output is 5 $(2 \times 3 - 1)$.

The transformation can be illustrated by using a **mapping** diagram like this:

You would describe this mapping by writing,

$x \longrightarrow 3x - 1$

This is read as 'x becomes $3x - 1$'

Graphs of the Form $x = a$ and $y = b$

A graph of the form $x = a$ is a vertical line with every x coordinate equal to a.

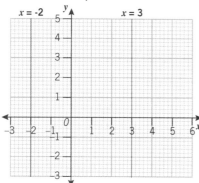

The line $x = -2$ has every x coordinate equal to -2.

A graph of the form $y = b$ is a horizontal line with every y coordinate equal to b.

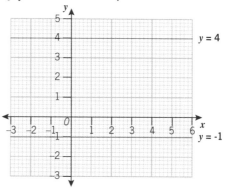

The line $y = 4$ has every y coordinate equal to 4.

LONSDALE

ESSENTIALS

Year 8
KS3 Mathematics
Coursebook Answers

NUMBERS

Page 7 – Quick Test

1. 20418
2. 15
3. False
4. 57
5. $2 \times 2 \times 3 \times 3$ or $2^2 \times 3^2$
6. 13104

Pages 8 – 9 – Skills Practice

1. 8 coaches and 22 seats left over
2. £16864
3. a) 6^5
   b) 2^6
   c) 8^4
4. a) $5 \times 5 \times 5 \times 5 \times 5 \times 5 \times 5 \times 5 \times 5$
   b) $10 \times 10 \times 10 \times 10 \times 10 \times 10 \times 10$
   c) $2 \times 2 \times 2 \times 3 \times 3 \times 3 \times 3 \times 3$
5. a) 17
   b) 6
   c) 450
   d) 67
   e) 553
6. a) 54
   b) 12
   c) 2
7. a) ± 8
   b) ± 9
   c) ± 13
   d) 25
   e) 64
   f) 9
8. a) 5×5 or 5^2
   b) $2 \times 2 \times 2 \times 2 \times 2$ or 2^5
   c) $2 \times 3 \times 3$ or 2×3^2
   d) $2 \times 2 \times 5 \times 5$ or $2^2 \times 5^2$
9. a) HCF = 2
      LCM = 420
   b) HCF = 4
      LCM = 144
10. £137.46

FRACTIONS, DECIMALS AND ESTIMATING

Page 15 – Quick Test

1. Hundredths
2. $7\frac{2}{5}$
3. B
4. True
5. 0.719, 0.72, 0.76, 3.21, 3.255, 3.26

Pages 16 – 17 – Skills Practice

1. a) $1\frac{1}{21}$
   b) $\frac{7}{33}$
   c) $\frac{3}{10}$
   d) $\frac{5}{6}$
   e) $\frac{8}{9}$
   f) $7\frac{15}{26}$
2. a) $\frac{6}{77}$
   b) $\frac{4}{9}$
   c) $\frac{5}{16}$
   d) $\frac{16}{45}$
   e) $\frac{6}{7}$
   f) $4\frac{7}{12}$
3. a) $\frac{11}{14}$
   b) $\frac{9}{11}$
   c) $1\frac{13}{27}$
   d) $2\frac{4}{7}$
   e) $1\frac{1}{2}$
   f) $2\frac{8}{17}$
4. £14000
5. 480
6. a) 4.02, 4.09, 4.26, 4.29, 4.293, 4.31
   b) 8.427, 8.429, 8.475, 8.48, 8.481, 8.73
   c) 6.902, 6.915, 6.92, 6.925, 6.926, 6.931
7. a) 1040
   b) 76.44
   c) 79.171
   d) 16.3
   e) 28.1
   f) 12
8. a) 16.43
   b) 9.37
   c) 12.87
   d) 3.43
   e) 8.71
   f) 146.93
9. a) 570
   b) 1380
   c) 0.631
   d) 2.79
   e) 0.027
   f) 15700
10. a) $8 \times 4 = 32$
    b) $10 \times 4 = 40$
    c) $6^2 = 36$
    d) $\dfrac{20 \times 40}{10} = \dfrac{800}{10} = 80$

NEGATIVE NUMBERS

Page 19 – Skills Practice

1. -2

2. a) -10, -6, -5, -4, -2, 0, 3, 4, 7
   b) -36, -12, -9, -7, -5, -4, 4, 6
   c) -41, -26, -13, -11, -10, -8, -3, 7

3. a) -9
   b) -3
   c) -5
   d) 4
   e) 9
   f) -2
   g) 35
   h) -38
   i) -53
   j) -1
   k) 1
   l) -10

4. a) 8
   b) 4
   c) -12
   d) 7
   e) 1
   f) -9
   g) 11
   h) -9
   i) -3
   j) -9
   k) -7
   l) 2

5. a) -21
   b) -12
   c) 20
   d) 21
   e) 5
   f) -5
   g) -50
   h) 5
   i) -42
   j) 64
   k) -20
   l) 25

6. a) -13
   b) -8
   c) 9
   d) -60
   e) 25
   f) -6
   g) 6
   h) -63

PERCENTAGES

Page 24 – Quick Test

1. Find 10% by dividing by 10 and then halve your answer to find 5%.

2. D

3. B

4. 77.5%

5. False

Page 25 – Skills Practice

1. 35

2. a) 50.4 miles
   b) £486.40
   c) 3034g
   d) 25.76cm

3. £337.84

4. 49.6%

5. $53.\dot{3}$%

6. 40.4% (1 d.p.)

7.

Garden furniture	60.8%
Bay tree	$66.\dot{6}$%
Plant pot	$277.\dot{7}$%

8. 25.3%

9. £224 640

10. 0.369, 37%, $\frac{2}{5}$, 0.409, 41%, $\frac{2}{3}$

11. £165.60

RATIO

Page 28 – Quick Test

1. False

2. C

3. £30 000

4. £1.96

5. True

Page 29 – Skills Practice

1. a) 4 : 5
   b) 1 : 2
   c) 3 : 1
   d) 3 : 7
   e) 5 : 9
   f) 5 : 3

2. 50 : 20 : 36 = 25 : 10 : 18

3. $\frac{1}{7}$

4. 7.2km

5. 32 blue beads

6. £35

7. 20 marbles

8. a) €395
   b) £55

9. 700ml

NUMBER PATTERNS AND SEQUENCES

Page 31 – Skills Practice

1. a) i) 11, 13
   ii) Add 2 each time
   b) i) 2, 0
   ii) Subtract 2 each time
   c) i) 50, 60
   ii) Add 10 each time
   d) i) 6.25, 3.125
   ii) Divide by 2 each time
   e) i) 48, 96
   ii) Multiply each preceding term by 2
   f) i) 8, 5
   ii) Subtract 3 each time

2. a)

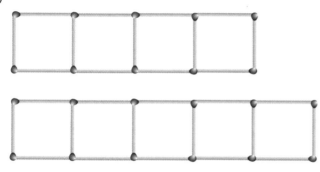

b)

Shape	1	2	3	4	5
Number of Matchsticks	4	7	10	13	16

c) 25
d) $3n + 1$

3. a) $2n$
   b) $2n + 1$
   c) $2n + 6$
   d) $2n + 3$
   e) $4n + 4$

4. a) ii) 12, 20, 28
   iii) Add 8 each time
   b) ii) 5, 9, 13
   iii) Add 4 each time
   c) ii) 13, 19, 25
   iii) Add 6 each time
   d) ii) 12, 22, 32
   iii) Add 10 each time

WORKING WITH ALGEBRA

Page 36 – Quick Test

1. $5abd$, alphabetical order, number first and no multiplication sign.

2. D

3. True

4. False

5. 42

Page 37 – Skills Practice

1. a) $4a$
   b) $11a - b$
   c) $x + 9y$
   d) $12y$
   e) $11c - 7d$
   f) $5xy - xy^2$

2. a) $8a^2$
   b) $18ab$
   c) $15de$
   d) $6b^2$
   e) $14a^2$
   f) $54p^2$
   g) $30a^2b$
   h) $6a^3$

3. a) $5x - 5$
   b) $3x + 6y$
   c) $6x - 12$
   d) $x^2 + 3x$
   e) $5x - 15 + 2x - 2 = 7x - 17$
   f) $12x - 48 - 3x + 3 = 9x - 45$

4. a) $5(3x - 1)$
   b) $10(2y + 1)$
   c) $3(x - 3y)$
   d) $x(x + 2)$
   e) $2y(7 - y)$
   f) $3(3y + 4)$

5. a) 19
   b) 10
   c) 20
   d) 9
   e) 35
   f) 28

6. a) $3x$
   b) $x - 5$
   c) $\frac{x}{2}$

EQUATIONS AND INEQUALITIES

Page 41 – Quick Test

1. True

2. B

3. False

4. C

5. a) $-3 < -1$
   b) $7 < 9$
   c) $6 > -6$
   d) $-5 < 4$

6. False

Pages 42 – 43 – Skills Practice

1. a) $x = 8$
    b) $x = 4$
    c) $x = 10$
    d) $x = 8$
    e) $x = 8$
    f) $x = 4$
    g) $x = 30$
    h) $x = 12$
    i) $x = 1$
    j) $x = 4$
    k) $x = -5$
    l) $x = -15$

2. a) $x = 2$
    b) $x = 4$
    c) $x = 4$
    d) $x = 8$
    e) $x = 2$
    f) $x = 5$
    g) $x = 4$
    h) $x = 7.5$
    i) $x = 2$
    j) $x = 8\frac{2}{3}$
    k) $x = 1\frac{1}{4}$
    l) $x = 11$

3. a) $x = \frac{4}{3} = 1\frac{1}{3}$
    b) $x = 2.5$
    c) $x = 9\frac{4}{5}$

4. a) $x = 2$
    b) $x = 9$
    c) $x = 1$
    d) $x = 3$
    e) $x = 8$
    f) $x = -3$
    g) $x = -3$
    h) $x = -\frac{9}{5} = -1\frac{4}{5}$

5. a) $x = 5$
    b) $x = 9$
    c) $x = 3$
    d) $x = 3$
    e) $x = 9$
    f) $x = 10$
    g) $x = -\frac{3}{4}$
    h) $x = -4$

6. $x = 2.76$

7. a) $5 < 9$
    b) $7 < 13$
    c) $15 > 8$
    d) $9 > 4$
    e) $7 < 17$

8. $6x + 16 = 40$
    $6x = 24$
    $x = 4$
    Length = 13cm
    Width = 7cm

9. $2n + 13 = 26$
    $2n = 13$
    $n = 6.5$

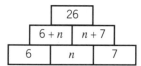

GRAPHS

Page 50 – Quick Test

1. Read across first then upwards or downwards.

2. True

3. False, $y = 2x$ is steeper

4. **B**

Page 51 – Skills Practice

1. a) i) $y = 3x$

x	-3	0	3
y	-9	0	9

   (ii) $y = x - 5$

x	-2	0	2
y	-7	-5	-3

   (iii) $y = 2x + 1$

x	-2	0	2
y	-3	1	5

   b)
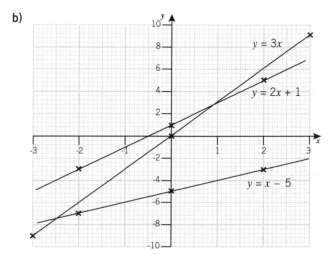

   c) i) $y = 3x$
       ii) $y = x - 5$
       iii) (0, 1)

SHAPES AND MEASURES

Page 56 – Quick Test

1. 6 faces

2. 9 edges

3. **D**

4. True

Page 57 – Skills Practice

1. A – Diameter
   B – Radius
   C – Tangent
   D – Circumference
   E – Arc

2.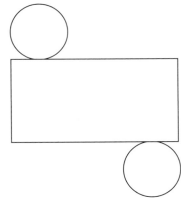

3. Triangle drawn accurately with lengths ±1mm

4. 5.5m

5. 30cm

ANGLES

Page 62 – Quick Test

1. 180°

2. False

3. True

4. 50°

5. C

Page 63 – Skills Practice

1. a) $a = 75°$
   b) $b = 157°$
   c) $a = 63°$
       $b = 117°$
       $c = 63°$
   d) $a = 112°$
   e) $a = 52°$
   f) $a = 84°$
   g) $a = 59°$
   h) $a = 54°$
       $b = 54°$
       $c = 126°$

2. a) Interior = 135°
   b) Exterior = 45°

3. a) 050°
   b) 230°

TRANSFORMATIONS

Page 66 – Quick Test

1. Translation, reflection, rotation and enlargement

2. True

3. False

4. True

Page 67 – Skills Practice

1.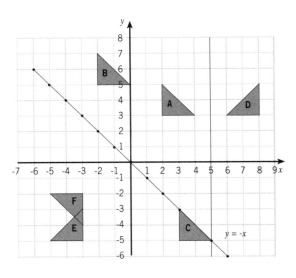

2.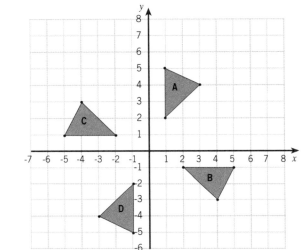

3.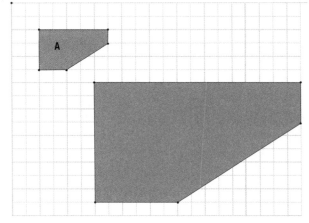

PERIMETER, AREA AND VOLUME

Page 72 – Quick Test

1. True

2. 5cm

3. 2cm

4. 3cm

5. False

Page 73 – Skills Practice

1. a) $24.5cm^2$
   b) $64.26cm^2$
   c) $161.85cm^2$
   d) $205cm^2$
   e) $132.75cm^2$
   f) $631.2cm^2$

2. a) i) 53.38cm
      ii) $226.87cm^2$
   b) i) 45.22cm
      ii) $162.78cm^2$
   c) i) 401.92cm
      ii) $12861.44cm^2$

3. $245.31cm^2$

4. Volume = $992cm^3$
   Surface area = $667.2cm^2$

HANDLING DATA

Page 78 – Quick Test

1. False

2. How many hours per day do you watch television?

3. True

4. Positive, negative and zero

5. a) Zero correlation
   b) Positive correlation
   c) Negative correlation
   d) Positive correlation

Page 79 – Skills Practice

1. What type of books do you read? Choose from this list:
   Fiction   ☐
   Non-fiction   ☐
   Crime   ☐
   Other   ☐

2. Angles: Vanilla 45°, Strawberry 120°, Chocolate 90°, Mint 105°

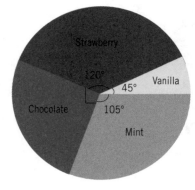

3.

	Walk	Car	Coach	Total
Boys	5	11	26	42
Girls	12	12	19	43
Total	17	23	45	85

4.

Stem	Leaf
2	5 5 6 7
3	2 7 8 9
4	1 1 6
5	8 8 9
6	2 5

Key 4|1 represents 41 seconds

AVERAGES

Page 82 – Quick Test

1. True

2. Highest value – lowest value

3. B

Page 83 – Skills Practice

1. a) Mean = 5.25
   b) Median = 5
   c) Mode = 5
   d) Range = 8

2. The averages for Paulo:
   Mean: 1.429
   Mode: 2
   Median: 2
   Range: 3

   The averages for Cesc:
   Mean: 1.571
   Mode: 1
   Median: 1
   Range: 2

   Nigel should choose Cesc. Cesc's mean score is higher than Paulo's and his range is smaller, so he is more consistent.

3. a) Mode = 3 Merits

   b) Range = 5 Merits

   c) Mean = 3.42 (2 d.p.) Merits

   d) Median = 3 Merits

4. a) 3.5 seconds

   b) 30.9 seconds

   c) 31.4 seconds

PROBABILITY

Page 86 – Quick Test

1. The likelihood that something will happen.

2. False

3. $\frac{2}{9}$

4. True

Page 87 – Skills Practice

1. a) $\frac{3}{9} = \frac{1}{3}$

   b) $\frac{4}{9}$

   c) $\frac{2}{9}$

   d) 0

2. 77%

3. 0.9

4. $\frac{3}{5}$

5. Geography, History
Geography, German
Geography, ICT
French, History
French, German
French, ICT
Technology, History
Technology, German
Technology, ICT

6.

Dice 2

+	1	2	3	4	5	6
1	2	3	4	5	6	7
2	3	4	5	6	7	8
3	4	5	6	7	8	9
4	5	6	**7**	**8**	**9**	**10**
5	6	7	**8**	**9**	**10**	**11**
6	7	8	**9**	**10**	**11**	12

Dice 1

   a) $\frac{2}{36} = \frac{1}{18}$

   b) $\frac{6}{36} = \frac{1}{6}$

   c) $\frac{1}{36}$

   d) 0

ACKNOWLEDGEMENTS

The author and publisher are grateful to the copyright holders for permission to use quoted materials and images.

Every effort has been made to trace copyright holders and obtain their permission for the use of copyright material. The author and publisher will gladly receive information enabling them to rectify any error or omission in subsequent editions. All facts are correct at time of going to press.

Published by Lonsdale
An imprint of HarperCollins*Publishers*
77–85 Fulham Palace Road
London W6 8JB

© 2009, 2011 Lonsdale.

ISBN: 978-1-906415-90-7

02/040211

Published by Lonsdale

Book concept and development: Helen Jacobs
Commissioning Editor: Rebecca Skinner
Author: Fiona Mapp
Project Editor: Emma Rae
Cover Design: Angela English
Inside Concept Design: Helen Jacobs and Sarah Duxbury
Text Design and Layout: Nicola Lancashire
Artwork: Lonsdale

Printed in the UK

Mixed Sources
Product group from well-managed forests and other controlled sources
www.fsc.org Cert no. SW-COC-001806
© 1996 Forest Stewardship Council

FSC is a non-profit international organisation established to promote the responsible management of the world's forests. Products carrying the FSC label are independently certified to assure consumers that they come from forests that are managed to meet the social, economic and ecological needs of present and future generations.

Find out more about HarperCollins and the environment at
www.harpercollins.co.uk/green

Drawing Straight Lined Graphs

To be able to draw any graph, the coordinates that lie on the graph need to be found.

Example
Draw the graphs of $y = x + 1$, $y = x - 3$ and $y = x + 5$ on the same axes.

1 $y = x + 1$

Choose some x coordinates, for example: $x = -2$, $x = 0$ and $x = 2$. You need at least 3 coordinates.

2 Draw up a table:

x	-2	0	2
y			

3 Substitute the values of x into the equation:

when $x = -2$
$y = -2 + 1 = -1$

when $x = 0$
$y = 0 + 1 = 1$

when $x = 2$
$y = 2 + 1 = 3$

Coordinate is (-2, -1) Coordinate is (0, 1) Coordinate is (2, 3)

x	-2	0	2
y	-1	1	3

4 Plot the set of three coordinates and join them with a straight line and label (below).

The table of values for the graphs $y = x - 3$ and $y = x + 5$ are:

$y = x - 3$

x	-2	0	2
y	-5	-3	-1

Coordinates (-2, -5) (0, -3) (2, -1)

$y = x + 5$

x	-2	0	2
y	3	5	7

Coordinates (-2, 3) (0, 5) (2, 7)

From these graphs we can see that they all have the same **gradient** (steepness). The point where the graph cuts the y axis (known as the **intercept** on the y axis) changes depending on the equation.

$y = x + 1$ intercepts the y axis at (0, 1)
$y = x - 3$ intercepts the y axis at (0, -3)
$y = x + 5$ intercepts the y axis at (0, 5)

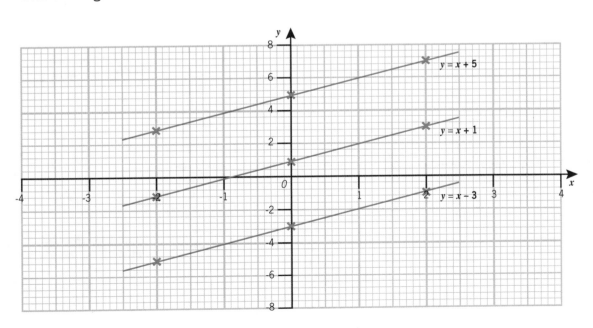

Graphs

The slope of a straight lined graph is known as the gradient of the line.

Example

Draw the graphs of:

a) $y = x$ **c)** $y = 3x$

b) $y = 2x$ **d)** $y = -2x$

1 Copy and complete the tables to work out the coordinates for each graph:

$y = x$

a)

x	-2	0	2
y	-2	0	2

(-2, -2) (0, 0) (2, 2)

$y = 3x$

c)

x	-2	0	2
y	-6	0	6

$y = 2x$

b)

x	-2	0	2
y	-4	0	4

(-2, -4) (0, 0) (2, 4)

$y = -2x$

d)

x	-2	0	2
y	4	0	-4

2 Draw the graphs:

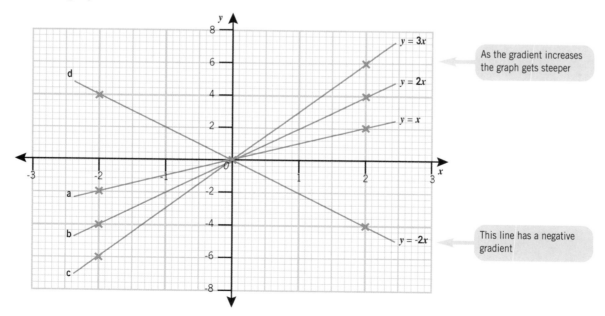

As the gradient increases the graph gets steeper

This line has a negative gradient

The number in front of x indicates the gradient:

- A line that slopes up from left to right has a positive gradient.
- A line that slopes down from left to right has a negative gradient.

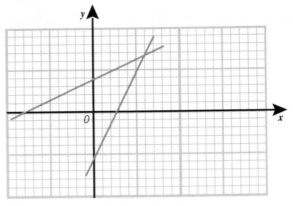

Positive Gradients

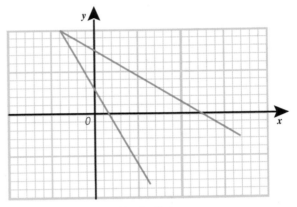

Negative Gradients

Graphs in the Form of $x + y = a$

When asked to draw a graph of the form $x + y = a$, work out the coordinates by choosing some x values.

Example

Draw the graph of $x + y = 6$

when $x = 0$	$y = 6$	$(0 + 6 = 6$ ✓$)$
when $x = 6$	$y = 0$	$(6 + 0 = 6$ ✓$)$
when $x = 2$	$y = 4$	$(2 + 4 = 6$ ✓$)$

So (0, 6) (6, 0) and (2, 4) lie on the graph $x + y = 6$

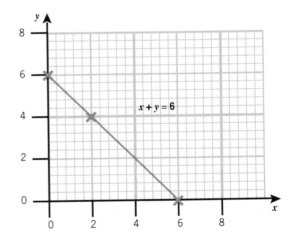

Graphs

Finding the Midpoint of a Line Segment

The diagram shows the straight line joining the points A (1, 1) and B (5, 5). A line joining two points is called a line segment.

The midpoint, M, of the line segment AB has coordinates (3, 3). In general, the midpoint of the line joining A (a, b) with B (s, t) is the point $\left(\dfrac{a + s}{2}, \dfrac{b + t}{2}\right)$.

In the example opposite the midpoint is $\left(\dfrac{1 + 5}{2}, \dfrac{1 + 5}{2}\right)$

$$= \left(\dfrac{6}{2}, \dfrac{6}{2}\right)$$

$$= (3, 3)$$

A computer graph-drawing package can be helpful when investigating gradients of straight lined graphs.

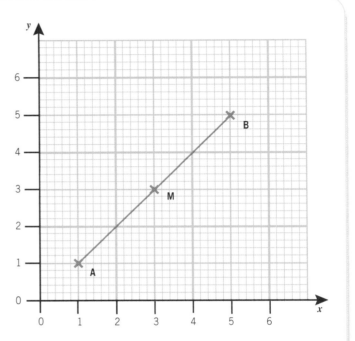

Conversion Graphs

Conversion graphs are used to change one unit of measurement to another unit, for example, litres to pints, km to miles and £ to $.

The exchange rate is very important when buying property overseas. In November 2007, the exchange rate for United Arab Emirates Dirhams (AED) was £1 = 7.4 AED. In November 2008 it was £1 = 5.7 AED. Buying an apartment for 600 000 AED in November 2007 would cost £81 081, but the same apartment in November 2008 would cost £105 263. A difference of £24 182!

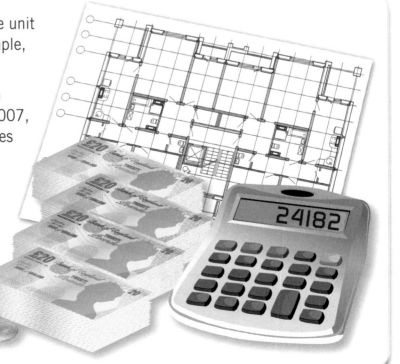

Curved Graphs of the Form $y = ax^2 + b$

You need to be able to draw graphs of more complicated equations.

Example

Draw the graphs of **a)** $y = x^2$ **b)** $y = 2x^2 - 1$ on the same axis.

1 Firstly work out a table of values. Choose some values of x:

$$y = x^2$$

x	-3	-2	-1	0	1	2	3
y	9	4	1	0	1	4	9

Work out the value of y for each value of x. If $x = -3$ then $y = (-3)^2 = 9$

The coordinates of the points of the curve are: (-3, 9) (-2, 4) (-1, 1) (0, 0) (1, 1) (2, 4) (3, 9)

$$y = 2x^2 - 1$$

x	-3	-2	-1	0	1	2	3
y	17	7	1	-1	1	7	17

Work out the value of y for each x coordinate. If $x = -3$ then $y = 2 \times -3^2 - 1$, $y = 17$

The coordinates of the points of the curve are: (-3, 17) (-2, 7) (-1, 1) (0, -1) (1, 1) (2, 7) (3, 17)

2 Plot each of the coordinates and join them with a smooth curve. Don't forget to label the curve.

The curve $y = 2x^2 - 1$ intercepts the y axis at (0, -1). The curve $y = x^2$ goes through the origin (0, 0).

Both graphs are symmetrical about the y axis.

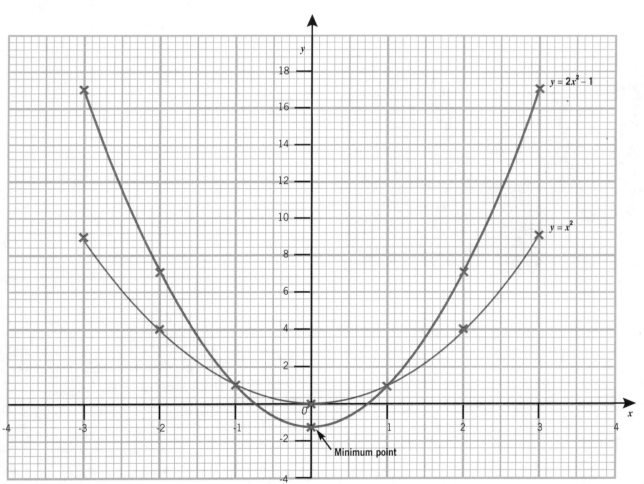

Graphs

Distance–Time Graphs

Distance–time graphs are often called **travel graphs**. Distance is on the **vertical** axis. Time is on the horizontal axis. These graphs can be used to represent journeys.

The gradient of the line is important. The steeper the line, the faster the speed.

A horizontal line indicates a rest or stop, because no distance is being travelled.

The speed can be found by dividing the distance by the time:

$$\text{Speed} = \frac{\text{Distance}}{\text{Time}}$$

Example

Matthew walks to the shops. He stops in the shops to buy some groceries. The graph shows his journey:

- Part A shows that Matthew walked to the shop 1200m away in 15 minutes.
- Part B shows that he stopped for 5 minutes in the shop.
- Part C is his return journey home. Since the slope of the graph is not as steep as part A, he's walking more slowly.
- Part D, Matthew stops for 2 minutes to tie his shoelaces.
- Part E, he continues his journey and arrives home 45 minutes after he set out.

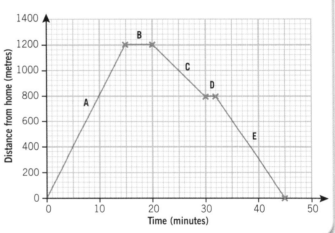

Quick Test

1. Explain how you read coordinates.
2. The vertical axis is called the y axis. True or false?
3. The graphs of $y = x$ and $y = 2x$ will have the same gradient. True or false?
4. The graph of $y = x - 4$ intercepts the y axis at:
   A (-4, 0) **B** (0, -4) **C** (4, 0) **D** (0, 4)

Skills Practice

1 a) Copy and complete the following tables:

(i) $y = 3x$

x	-3	0	3
y			

(ii) $y = x - 5$

x	-2	0	2
y			

(iii) $y = 2x + 1$

x	-2	0	2
y			

b) Copy the following axes onto graph paper. On your axes, plot the values from the tables you completed in a).

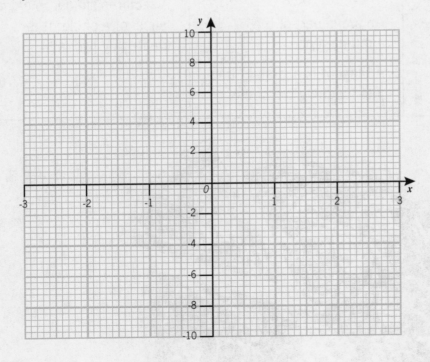

c) From the graphs you have drawn:
  i) Which graph is the steepest?
  ii) Which graph cuts the y axis at (0, -5)?
  iii) What is the y-intercept of the graph $y = 2x + 1$?

Shapes and Measures

The Circle

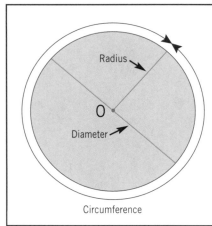 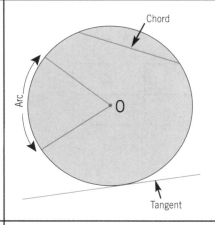 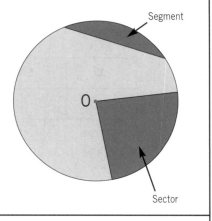

The **circumference** is the distance around the outside edge of a circle. The **diameter** is twice the **radius**.	A **chord** is a line that joins two points on the circumference. A chord does not go through the centre (O). An **arc** is part of the circumference. A **tangent** is a straight line, just touching the circle.	A **segment** is part of a circle separated by a chord. A **sector** is similar to a 'slice' of a circle. It is created by two radii.

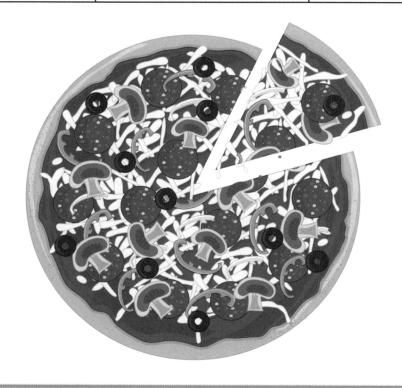

3D Solids and Nets

The net of a 3D solid is a 2D (flat) shape that can be folded to make a 3D solid:

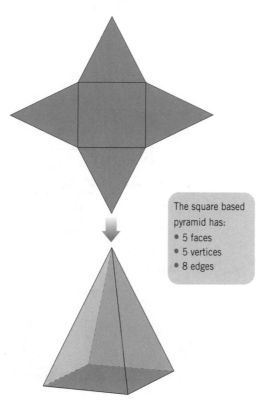

The square based pyramid has:
- 5 faces
- 5 vertices
- 8 edges

Examples

a) You can represent 3D shapes on isometric paper. On this paper you can draw lengths in three perpendicular directions on the same scale. The faces do not appear in their true shape.

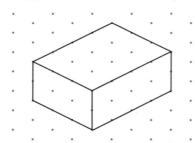

b) The 'T' shaped prism can be shown clearly on isometric paper.

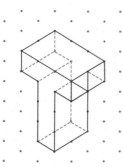

Quadrilaterals

Quadrilaterals have four sides.

There are several types of quadrilateral:

Square
- All angles are 90°.
- All sides are equal.
- Four lines of symmetry.
- Rotational symmetry of order 4.

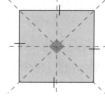

Rectangle
- All angles are 90°.
- Opposite sides are equal.
- Two lines of symmetry.
- Rotational symmetry of order 2.

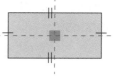

Parallelogram
- No lines of symmetry.
- Rotational symmetry of order 2.
- Opposite sides are parallel and equal in length.
- Opposite angles are equal.

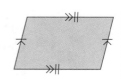

Rhombus
- Two lines of symmetry.
- Rotational symmetry of order 2.
- All sides are equal in length.
- Opposite sides are parallel.
- Opposite angles are equal.

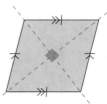

Kite
- One line of symmetry.
- No rotational symmetry.
- Has two pairs of adjacent sides equal in length.

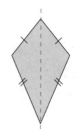

Trapezium
- One pair of parallel sides.
- No lines of symmetry unless it's an isosceles trapezium.
- No rotational symmetry.
- Non-parallel sides equal in length (isosceles trapezium only).

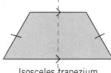

Isosceles trapezium

Shapes and Measures

Plans and Elevations

A **plan** is what can be seen when a 3D solid is viewed from above.

An **elevation** is seen if the 3D solid is looked at from the side or front view.

Plans are often used in the construction industry.

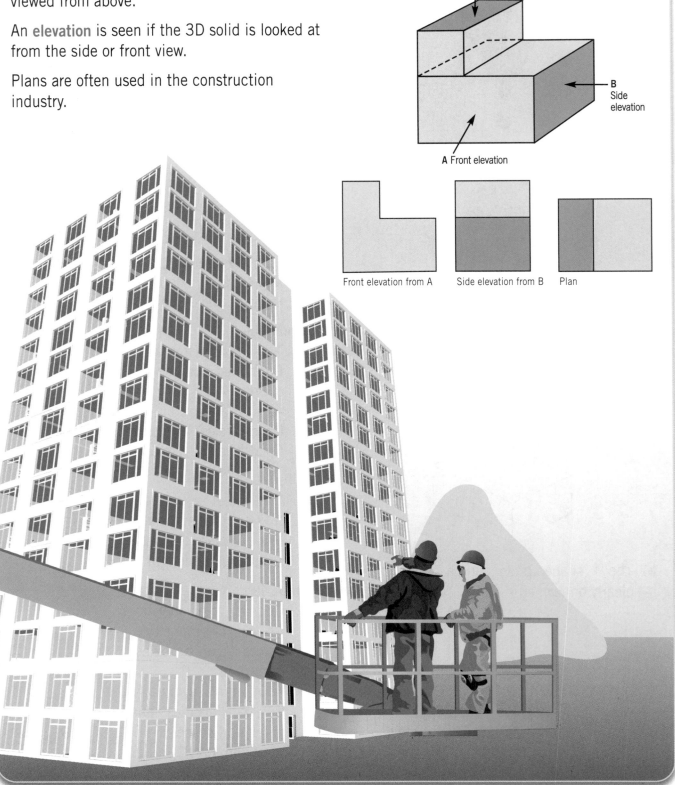

Plan

B
Side
elevation

A Front elevation

Front elevation from A   Side elevation from B   Plan

Constructions

When asked to construct shapes and lines, use a compass, ruler and protractor.

Examples
Use a compass to construct these triangles.

1 • Draw the longest side.
 • With the compass point at A, draw an arc of radius 5cm.
 • With the compass point at B, draw an arc of radius 7cm.
 • Join A and B to the point where the two arcs meet at C.

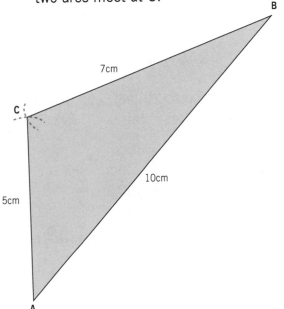

2 • Draw the line AB.
 • Measure the angle B as 39°.
 • Draw the line BC.
 • Join C to A by drawing a line.

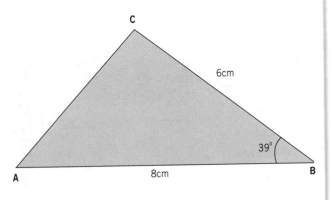

Scale Drawings

A **scale drawing** is very useful for finding lengths that can't be measured directly.

Architects and surveyors use scale drawings to show house and development plans.

Models of buildings are often used when property developments are launched. This gives buyers an idea of what a development might look like.

Example
A house plan has a scale of 1 : 20. If the width of the house on the plan is 72cm, what is the width of the real house?

1cm represents 20cm

72cm represents 72 × 20 = 1440cm

1440cm = 14.4m

The width of the house is 14.4m.

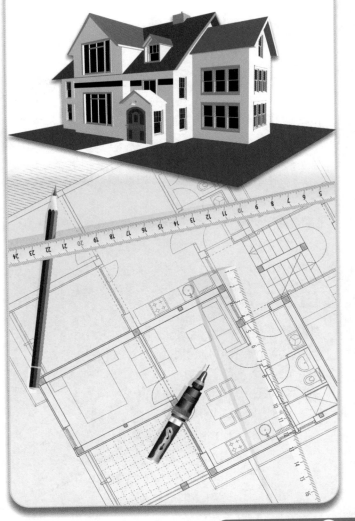

Shapes and Measures

Metric and Imperial Units

The table shows some approximate comparisons between **metric** and **imperial units**.

Length	2.5cm ≈ 1 inch 30cm ≈ 1 foot 1m ≈ 39 inches 8km ≈ 5 miles
Mass	25g ≈ 1 ounce 1 kg ≈ 2.2 pounds
Capacity	1l ≈ $1\frac{3}{4}$ pints 4.5l ≈ 1 gallon

Examples

1 Change 60km into miles.

8km = 5 miles

so 1km = $\frac{5}{8}$ mile

60km = 60 × $\frac{5}{8}$ mile

= 37.5 miles

2 A patio measures 20 feet. Approximately how many metres is this?

1 foot	= 30cm
30cm × 20cm	= 600cm
20 feet	= 600cm
600cm	= 6m

The patio is approximately 6 metres long.

Quick Test

1 How many faces does a cuboid have?

2 How many edges does a triangular prism have?

3 Approximately how many pounds is in 3.5kg?

   A 6.5 pounds   **C** 5.9 pounds

   B 8.4 pounds   **D** 7.7 pounds

4 The diameter of a circle is twice the radius. True or false?

Skills Practice

1 Draw lines from the labels to match them with the parts of the circle:

Radius

Arc

Circumference

Tangent

Diameter

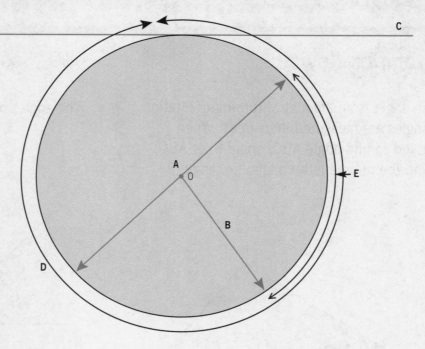

2 Draw the net of this cylinder.

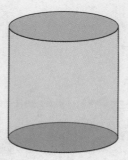

3 Accurately construct this triangle, using a ruler and compass only.

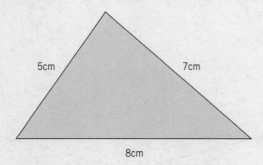

5cm   7cm

8cm

4 A plan of a building has a scale of 1 : 100. If the width of the building on the plan is 5.5cm, how many metres is the actual building?

5 Approximately what is 12 inches in centimetres?

Angles

Angles Revision

An **angle** is an amount of turning or rotation. Angles are measured in **degrees**. When asked to find angle ABC, angle B, or ABC, find the middle letter angle, i.e. angle B.

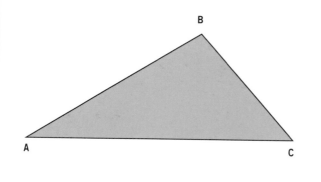

Angles on a Straight Line

The angles on a straight line add up to 180°.

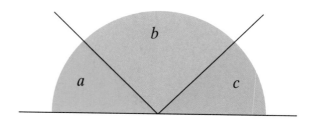

$a + b + c = 180°$

Angles at a Point

The angles at a point add up to 360°.

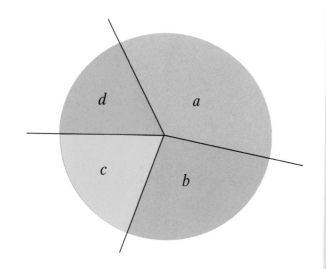

$a + b + c + d = 360°$

Vertically Opposite Angles

Vertically opposite angles are equal.

$a = b$

$c = d$

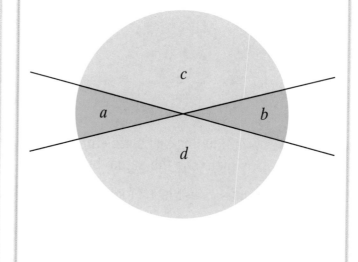

Angles in a Triangle

The angles in a triangle add up to 180°.

$a + b + c = 180°$

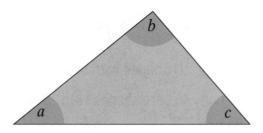

Any exterior angle of a triangle is equal to the sum of the two opposite interior angles.

$a + b = c$

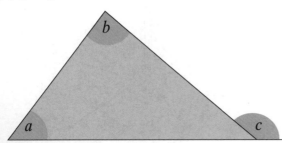

Examples

Work out the size of angle x in each of these triangles:

1

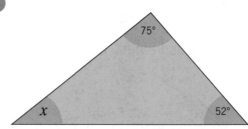

$x + 75° + 52° = 180°$
$x + 127° = 180°$
$x = 53°$

2

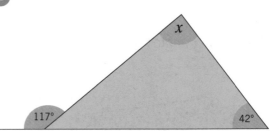

$x + 42° = 117°$
$x = 117° - 42°$
$x = 75°$

3 Since the base angles are equal in an isosceles triangle:

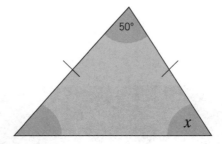

$2x + 50° = 180°$
$2x = 130°$
$x = 65°$

Angles

Angles in a Quadrilateral

The angles in a quadrilateral add up to 360°.

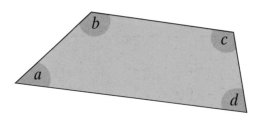

$a + b + c + d = 360°$

Example

Find the missing angles in this quadrilateral.

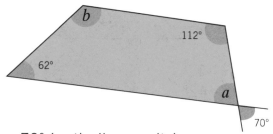

$a = 70°$ (vertically opposite)
$b + 70° + 112° + 62° = 360°$
$$b + 244° = 360°$$
$$b = 116°$$

Angles in a Polygon

Polygons are 2D shapes with straight sides.

Regular polygons are shapes with all sides and angles equal.

There are two types of angles in any polygon: **interior** (inside) and **exterior** (outside).

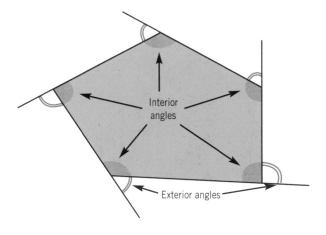

For a regular polygon…
* the sum of the exterior angles adds up to 360°
* for 'n' exterior angles, size of an exterior angle $= \frac{360°}{n}$
* interior angle + exterior angle = 180°
* sum of the interior angles $= (n - 2) \times 180°$ or $(2n - 4) \times 90°$

Examples

① A regular polygon has 8 sides. What is the size of the interior angle?

$n = 8$, so exterior angle $= \frac{360°}{8} = 45°$

Since the exterior angle + interior angle = 180°

Interior angle $= 180° - 45°$

$= 135°$

2 Work out the size of angle x in this pentagon.

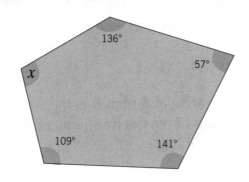

Sum of the interior angles $= (n - 2) \times 180°$
$= (5 - 2) \times 180°$
$= 540°$
$x + 136° + 57° + 109° + 141° = 540°$
$x + 443° = 540°$
$x = 540° - 443°$
$x = 97°$

Angles in Parallel Lines

a) **Alternate angles** are equal.

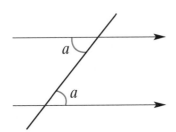

b) **Corresponding angles** are equal.

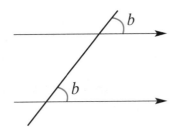

c) **Supplementary angles** add up to 180°.
$c + d = 180°$

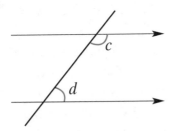

Examples
Find the angles labelled by letters in the diagrams below:

1

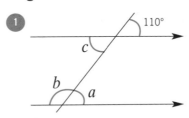

$a = 110°$ (corresponding)
$b = 70°$ (angles on a straight line)
$c = 110°$ (vertically opposite)

2

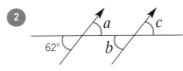

$a = 62°$ (vertically opposite)
$b = 62°$ (alternate and corresponding)
$c = 62°$ (vertically opposite)

3

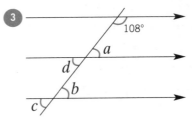

$a = 180° - 108°$
$= 72°$ (supplementary)
$b = 72°$ (corresponding)
$c = 72°$ (vertically opposite)
$d = 72°$ (alternate)

Angles not drawn to scale

Angles

Bearings

A **bearing** is the direction travelled between two points, given as an angle in degrees.

Aeroplanes and ships use bearings when travelling on a journey. This helps to avoid collisions as each plane flies on a particular bearing at a particular speed and altitude (height).

All bearings are measured from the North line in a clockwise direction. They are always written as three figures.

Examples

1 Use a protractor to measure the bearing of:
  a) A from B
  b) B from A

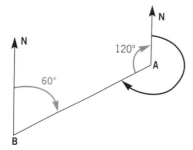

a) The bearing of **A from B** is the angle measured from the North line at B (shown in red) = 60°

Bearing = 060°

b) The bearing of **B from A** is the angle measured from the North line at A (shown in black) = 240°

This could be calculated since both North lines are parallel lines.

180° − 60° = 120°

The bearing of B from A is 360° − 120° = 240°

2 The bearing of P from Q is 130°

The bearing of Q from P is 360° − 50° = 310°

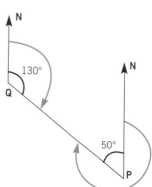

Quick Test

1 What do the angles in a triangle add up to?
2 Bearings are measured in an anticlockwise direction. True or false?
3 Supplementary angles add up to 180°. True or false?
4 Three angles in a quadrilateral add up to 310°. What is the size of the fourth angle?
5 A five-sided polygon is called a...
  A hexagon   C pentagon
  B nonagon   D octagon

1 Work out the size of the missing angles:

a)

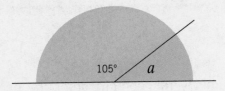

b)

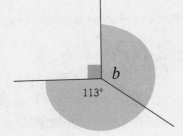

c)

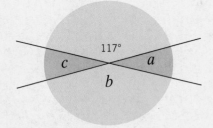

d)

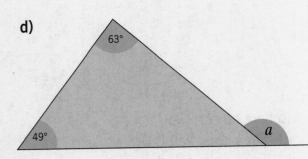

e)

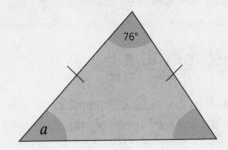

f)

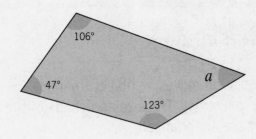

g)

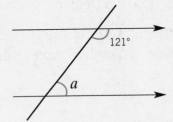

h)

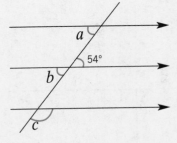

2 Work out the size of **a)** the interior and **b)** the exterior angles of a regular octagon.

3 **a)** Write down the bearing of D from C.
b) Work out the bearing of C from D.

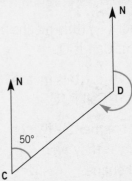

Transformations

Transformations

A **transformation** changes the position or size of a shape. There are four types of transformations: **translation**, **reflection**, **rotation** and **enlargement**.

There are several geometry computer packages that can be used to explore transformations.

Translation

A translation moves an object from one place to another. The size and shape of the **object** are not changed.

Vectors can be used to describe the distance and direction of a transformation.

The vector is written as $\binom{a}{b}$. 'a' represents the **horizontal** movement and 'b' represents the **vertical** movement.

Example

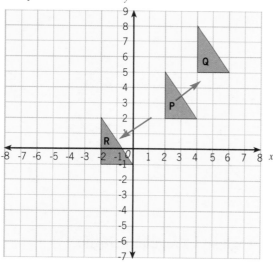

1. Translate P by the vector $\binom{2}{3}$ (this means 2 to the right and 3 up). Call it Q.

2. Translate P by the vector $\binom{-4}{-3}$ (this means 4 to the left and 3 down). Call it R.

Triangles P, Q and R are **congruent** – two or more shapes are congruent if they have exactly the same size and shape.

Reflection

A reflection creates an image of an object on the other side of the **mirror line**. The mirror line is known as an **axis of reflection**. The size and shape of the object are not changed.

Example

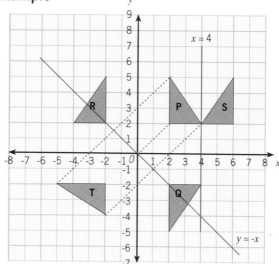

Reflect object P in:
a) The x axis, call it Q.
b) The y axis, call it R.
c) The line $x = 4$, call it S.
d) The line $y = -x$, call it T.

All the triangles are congruent.

Transformations in Art

Transformations have been used by artists and designers for thousands of years. Many patterns go around in a circle. Rose windows are particularly characteristic of Gothic architecture and may be seen in all the major Gothic cathedrals of Northern France. Their origins are much earlier and rose windows can be seen in the medieval period.

Rotations

A rotation turns a object through an angle about a fixed point. This fixed point is called the **centre of rotation**. The size and shape of the object are not changed.

Example
Rotate P:

a) 90° clockwise about (0,0), call it Q.

b) 180° clockwise about (0,0), call it S.

c) 90° anticlockwise about (0,1), call it T.

When describing a rotation give:

i) The angle of the turn.

ii) The direction of the turn.

iii) The centre of rotation.

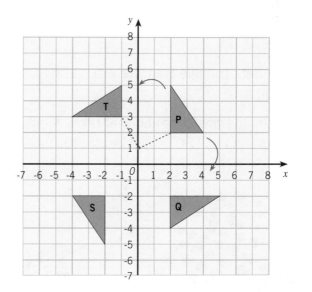

Enlargements

An enlargement changes the size but not the shape of an object.

The **centre of enlargement** is the point from which the enlargement takes place.

The **scale factor** indicates how many times the lengths of the original figure have increased in size. If the scale factor is greater than 1 the shape becomes bigger. If the scale factor is less than 1 the shape becomes smaller.

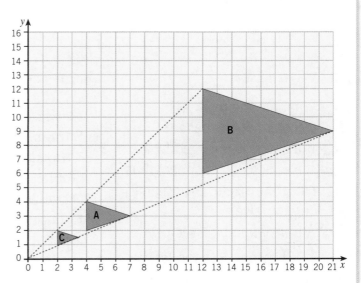

Example

1 Enlarge triangle A by a scale factor of 3 to give triangle B, centre (0,0).

2 Enlarge triangle A by a scale factor of $\frac{1}{2}$ to give triangle C, centre (0,0).

Triangle B is three times the size of triangle A. Triangle C is half the size of triangle A.

Transformations

Transformations can be combined in a series of two or more transformations.

Example

1 Reflect triangle A in the x axis and call it B.

2 Reflect triangle B in the y axis and call it C.

The single transformation that takes A onto C is a rotation of 180° about centre (0,0).

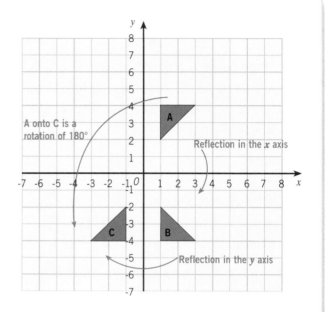

A onto C is a rotation of 180°

Reflection in the x axis

Reflection in the y axis

Quick Test

1 What are the four transformations called?

2 If a shape is enlarged by a scale factor 2, each length is twice the size of the original. True or false?

3 A translation by a vector $\begin{pmatrix} -3 \\ -6 \end{pmatrix}$ means 3 to the left and 6 up. True or false?

4 A translation by a vector $\begin{pmatrix} 3 \\ -2 \end{pmatrix}$ means 3 to the right and 2 down. True or false?

KEY WORDS

Make sure you understand these words before moving on!

- Transformation
- Translation
- Reflection
- Rotation
- Enlargement
- Object
- Vector
- Horizontal
- Vertical
- Congruent
- Mirror line
- Axis of reflection
- Centre of rotation
- Centre of enlargement
- Scale factor

Skills Practice

1 Copy the coordinate axes opposite.

  a) Translate triangle A by the vector $\begin{pmatrix} -4 \\ 2 \end{pmatrix}$. Call it B.

  b) Translate triangle A by the vector $\begin{pmatrix} 1 \\ -8 \end{pmatrix}$. Call it C.

  c) Reflect triangle A in the line $x = 5$. Call it D.

  d) Reflect triangle C in the y axis. Call it E.

  e) Reflect triangle A in the line $y = -x$. Call it F.

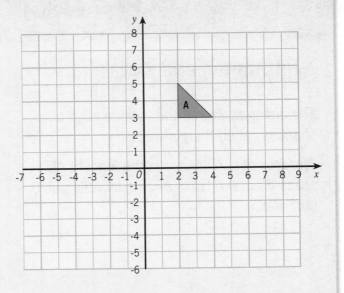

2 Copy the coordinate axes opposite.

  a) Rotate triangle A by 90° clockwise about (0,0). Call it B.

  b) Rotate triangle A by 90° anticlockwise about (0,0). Call it C.

  c) Rotate triangle A 180° about (0,0). Call it D.

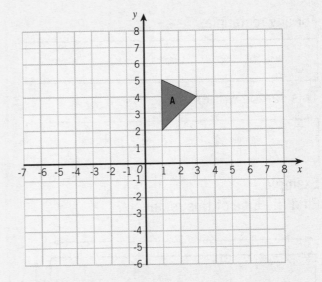

3 On a separate piece of paper enlarge shape A with a scale factor of 3 about point P.

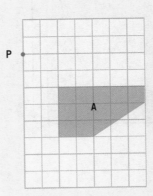

Perimeter, Area and Volume

Perimeter and Area

The distance around the outside edge of a shape is called the **perimeter**.

The **area** of a 2D shape is the amount of space it covers. Units of area include mm^2, cm^2 and m^2.

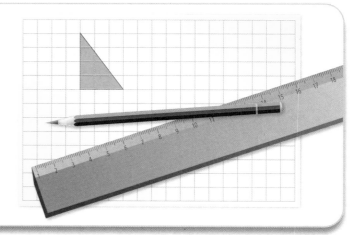

Area of a Rectangle

For any rectangle:

Area	=	Length	×	Width

This can be written as:

$$A = l \times w$$

Example
Find the area of this rectangle.

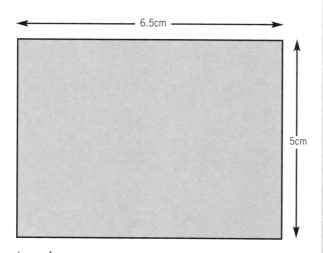

6.5cm

5cm

$A = l \times w$
  $= 6.5 \times 5$
  $= 32.5cm^2$

Area of a Triangle

The area of a triangle is:

Area	=	$\frac{1}{2}$	×	Base	×	Perpendicular height

This can be written as:

$$A = \tfrac{1}{2} \times b \times h$$

Example
Find the area of this triangle.

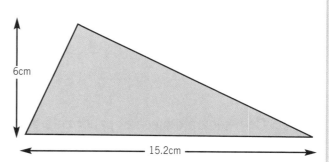

6cm

15.2cm

$A = \frac{1}{2} \times b \times h$
  $= \frac{1}{2} \times 15.2 \times 6$
  $= 45.6cm^2$

Area of a Parallelogram

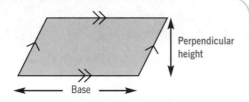

Area	=	Base	×	Perpendicular height

This can be written as:

$$A = b \times h$$

Example
Find the area of this parallelogram.

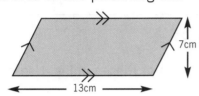

$$\begin{aligned} A &= b \times h \\ &= 13 \times 7 \\ &= 91 \text{cm}^2 \end{aligned}$$

Area of a Trapezium

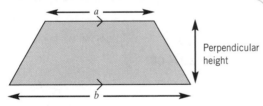

The area of a trapezium is:

Area	=	$\frac{1}{2}$	×	(Sum of parallel sides)	×	Perpendicular height between them

Example
Find the area of the trapezium.

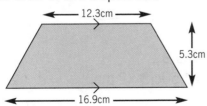

$$A = \frac{1}{2} \times (a+b) \times h$$

$$\begin{aligned} A &= \frac{1}{2} \times (12.3 + 16.9) \times 5.3 \\ &= 77.38 \text{cm}^2 \end{aligned}$$

Area of Compound Shapes

Compound shapes are made up of different sized shapes. The area can be worked out in parts.

Example
A sewing pattern is this shape.

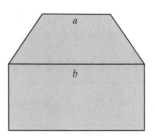

The sewing pattern can be split up into a rectangle (2) and a trapezium (1). The area of each one can then be worked out.

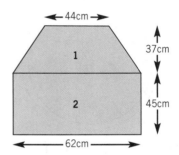

$$\begin{aligned} \text{Area of 1} &= \frac{1}{2} \times (a+b) \times h \\ &= \frac{1}{2} \times (44+62) \times 37 \\ &= 1961 \text{cm}^2 \end{aligned}$$

$$\begin{aligned} \text{Area of 2} &= l \times w \\ &= 62 \times 45 \\ &= 2790 \text{cm}^2 \end{aligned}$$

$$\begin{aligned} \text{Total Area} &= 2790 + 1961 \\ &= 4751 \text{cm}^2 \end{aligned}$$

Perimeter, Area and Volume

Circumference of a Circle

The **circumference** of a circle is the distance around the outside edge.

The circumference is found by:

$$C = \pi \times \text{Diameter}$$

or

$$C = \pi \times 2 \times \text{Radius}$$

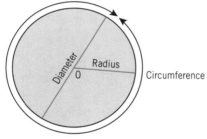

Remember: The **radius** is half the **diameter**.

This can be written as:

$$C = \pi d \quad \text{or} \quad C = 2\pi r$$

π is one of the most important numbers in mathematics and is widely used in Geometry. In Greek the name of this letter is pronounced 'pi'. The value of π has been calculated to more than a trillion (10^{12}) digits. We usually use π to 2 or 3 decimal places. π = 3.14 (2 d.p.)

Examples
Find the circumference of these circles. Use π = 3.14

a)

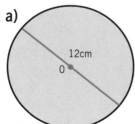

b)

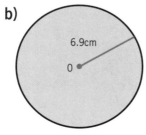

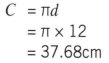

$$C = \pi d$$
$$= \pi \times 12$$
$$= 37.68\text{cm}$$

$$C = 2\pi r$$
$$= 2 \times \pi \times 6.9$$
$$= 43.33\text{cm (2 d.p.)}$$

Area of a Circle

The area of a circle is found by:

$$\text{Area} = \pi \times \text{Radius}^2$$

Which is written as:

$$A = \pi r^2$$

Examples
Find the area of these circles. Use π = 3.14

a)

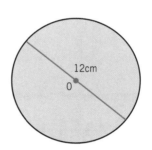

$$A = \pi r^2$$
$$= \pi \times 6^2 \quad \longleftarrow \text{Remember } 6^2 = 6 \times 6$$
$$= 113.04\text{cm}^2$$

b)

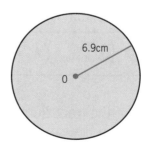

$$A = \pi r^2$$
$$= \pi \times 6.9^2$$
$$= 149.50\text{cm}^2 \text{ (2 d.p.)}$$

Volume and Surface Area of a Cuboid

The **volume** of an object is the amount of space it occupies. Units of volume include mm^3, cm^3 and m^3. A cuboid is a solid with rectangular faces.

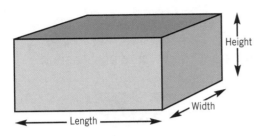

Volume of a cuboid	=	Length	×	Width	×	Height

This can be written as:

$$V = l \times w \times h$$

To find the **surface area** of a cuboid it is best to consider the net of the cuboid.

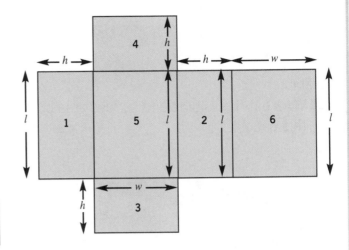

Faces 1 and 2: $A = (l \times h) \times 2$
$A = 2(h \times l)$

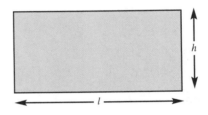

Faces 5 and 6: $A = (l \times w) \times 2$
$A = 2(l \times w)$

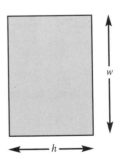

Faces 3 and 4: $A = (h \times w) \times 2$
$A = 2(h \times w)$

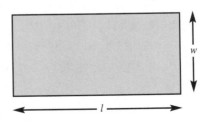

Total surface area	=	$2hl$	×	$2hw$	×	$2lw$

Perimeter, Area and Volume

Volume and Surface Area of a Cuboid (cont.)

Examples

1 Work out the volume and surface area of this cuboid.

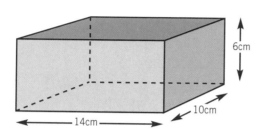

$$\text{Volume} = l \times w \times h$$
$$= 14 \times 10 \times 6$$
$$= 840 \text{cm}^3$$

$$\text{Surface area} = 2hl + 2hw + 2lw$$
$$= (2 \times 6 \times 14) + (2 \times 6 \times 10)$$
$$+ (2 \times 14 \times 10)$$
$$= 168 + 120 + 280$$
$$= 568 \text{cm}^2$$

2 Work out the volume of this solid.

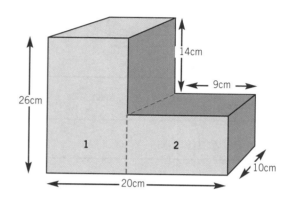

Draw a dashed line to split the solid in two:

$$\text{Volume of 1: } V = l \times w \times h$$
$$= 11 \times 10 \times 26$$
$$= 2860 \text{cm}^3$$

$$\text{Volume of 2: } V = l \times w \times h$$
$$= 9 \times 10 \times 12$$
$$= 1080 \text{cm}^3$$

$$\text{Total volume} = 2860 + 1080$$
$$= 3940 \text{cm}^3$$

Quick Test

1 cm^3 is a unit of volume. True or false?

2 A rectangle has an area of 40cm^2. If the height is 8cm, what is the width?

3 The volume of a cuboid is 64cm^3. If the height is 8cm and the width 4cm, what is the length?

4 The volume of a cube is 27cm^3. What is the length of each side?

5 To find the area of a trapezium you use this formula: $A = \frac{1}{2}(a \times b) + h$. True or false?

Skills Practice

1 Find the area of each of these shapes:

a)

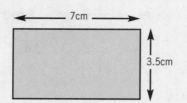

7cm
3.5cm

c)

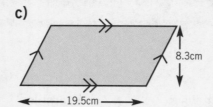

8.3cm
19.5cm

e)

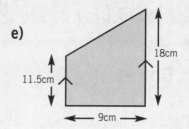

18cm
11.5cm
9cm

b)

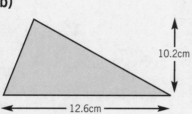

10.2cm
12.6cm

d)

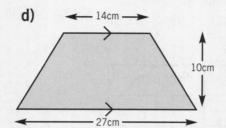

14cm
10cm
27cm

f)

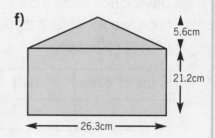

5.6cm
21.2cm
26.3cm

2 For these circles, work out using π = 3.14 to 2 d.p. the:
i) Circumference
ii) Area

a)

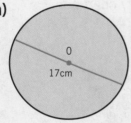

0
17cm

b)

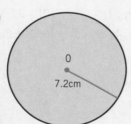

0
7.2cm

c)

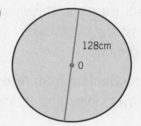

128cm
0

3 Work out the area of this semicircle. Use π = 3.14 and give your answer to 2 d.p.

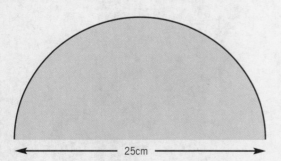

25cm

4 Find the volume and surface area of this cuboid.

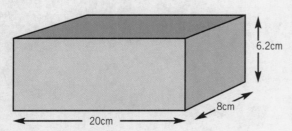

6.2cm
20cm
8cm

Handling Data

Collecting Data

Data can be collected in several ways.

1 **Observation** using a **data collection sheet**. For example, collecting data on the types of books people read.

Type of Book	Tally	Frequency

2 **Experiments** can be used to collect data. For example, throwing a die 60 times to test the hypothesis 'A six is least likely to come up'.

3 **Information from resources** e.g. books, newspapers and Internet.

4 **Questionnaires** are often used to find out information.

The **census** is a survey of the whole population in England and Wales. It takes place every 10 years. The next one will take place in 2011. The census collects data on population, transport, health, housing and employment.

The information is used to help the government plan the future running of the country.

When writing questionnaires:
- Keep the questions simple.
- Make sure your personal opinion doesn't show.
- Allow for all possible outcomes.

Example

How many hours of sport to the nearest hour do you do per week?

Under 2 ☐

2 – 4 ☐

5 – 7 ☐

More than 7 ☐

Discrete data is usually found by counting. **Continuous data** is usually found by measuring.

Data that has been collected can be put into a table called a tally chart or frequency table.

Representing Data

Data can be represented using pictograms, bar charts and bar line graphs for discrete data.

When there is a large amount of data, the data is often grouped, e.g., 1 – 5, 6 – 10, 11 – 15, etc for discrete data. Continuous data is put into **class intervals**, usually of equal width.

Example
The table below shows information about the height of 40 people.

$155 \leqslant h < 160$ means a height of 155cm or more, but less than 160cm.

The class widths here are 5cm.

This data can be put into a **frequency diagram**. This is similar to a bar chart but since it represents continuous data there are no gaps between the bars. This is sometimes known as a **histogram**.

Height, h (cm)	Frequency
$155 \leqslant h < 160$	4
$160 \leqslant h < 165$	6
$165 \leqslant h < 170$	15
$170 \leqslant h < 175$	7
$175 \leqslant h < 180$	8

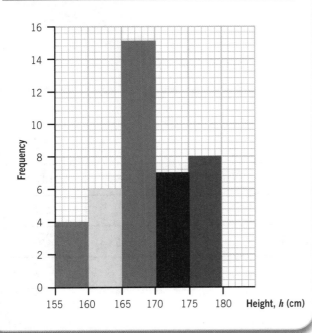

Interpreting Pie Charts

In a **pie chart**, the data is shown in a circle that is split up into sections. Each section represents a certain number of items.

Example
90 students were asked where they went on holiday in the summer. The pie chart shows the result of this survey.

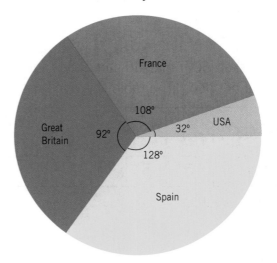

We can see that Spain is the most popular holiday destination.

$\dfrac{108°}{360°} \times 90 = 27$ — 27 students went on holiday to France

$\dfrac{32°}{360°} \times 90 = 8$ — 8 students went on holiday to the USA

Handling Data

Drawing Pie Charts

To draw a pie chart:
- Draw a circle and mark the centre.
- Work out the angles.

Example

Toby asked 30 friends to name their favourite flavour of crisps. The table shows his results:

Flavour	Bacon	Beef	Cheese	Plain	Salt n' Vinegar
Frequency	5	5	7	3	10

Draw a pie chart.

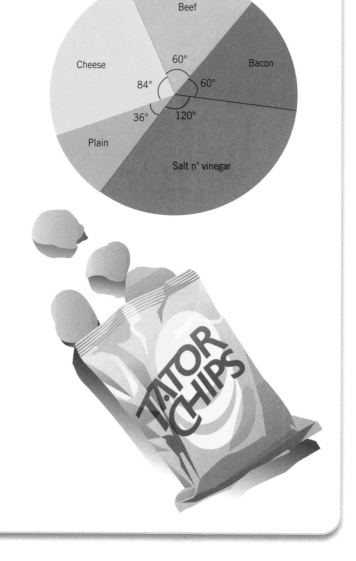

Method 1

$\frac{5}{30} \times 360° = 60°$ (5 out of 30 students chose Bacon and 5 chose Beef).

$\frac{7}{30} \times 360° = 84°$ (Cheese)

$\frac{10}{30} \times 360° = 120°$ (Salt n' Vinegar)

$\frac{3}{30} \times 360° = 36°$ (Plain)

Method 2

$360° \div 30 = 12°$ (12° represents 1 student.
Multiply each frequency by 12°).
Angle for Bacon and Beef is $12° \times 5 = 60°$
Angle for Plain is $12° \times 3 = 36°$
Angle for Cheese is $12° \times 7 = 84°$
Angle for Salt n' Vinegar is $12° \times 10 = 120°$

Two-Way Tables

A two-way table contains information that is totalled in both directions.

Example

Here is a two-way table showing the number of adults in a numeracy and literacy class.

There are 12 men in the numeracy class.
There are 25 women in total.

	Numeracy	Literacy	Total
Male	12	7	19
Female	15	10	25
Total	27	17	44

Scatter Diagrams and Correlation

A **scatter diagram** (scatter graph) is used to show two sets of data at the same time.

A scatter diagram is also used to show the **correlation** (connection) between two sets of data.

Types of correlation:

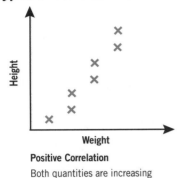

Positive Correlation

Both quantities are increasing

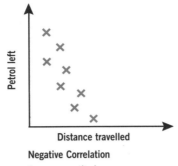

Negative Correlation

As one quantity increases, the other decreases

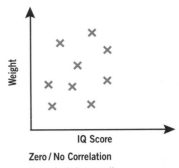

Zero / No Correlation

There is little or no linear relationship between the variables

Drawing a Scatter Diagram

Example

The table shows the height in cm and weight in kg of 10 women.

Work out the scales first and plot the points carefully. Each time a point is plotted, tick it off.

Height (cm)	155	158	154	164	165	161	157	159	161	161
Weight (kg)	57 ✓	57 ✓	54 ✓	62 ✓	67 ✓	65 ✓	60 ✓	62 ✓	64 ✓	61 ✓

The scatter diagram is used to show this information:

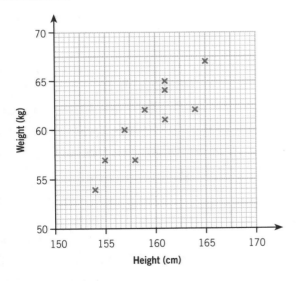

There is a positive correlation. The taller the women are the more they weigh.

Line of best fit is a line that best fits the data. There is roughly the same number of points above and below the line.

A line of best fit is used to make predictions.

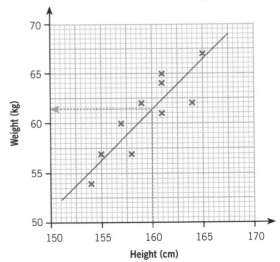

Using a line of best fit, a woman of 160cm in height is approximately 61.5kg.

Scatter diagrams can be drawn using a spreadsheet package on the computer.

Handling Data

Stem and Leaf Diagrams

A **stem and leaf diagram** is used for recording and displaying information.

The stem often represents tens and the leaves represent the units.

Stem and leaf diagrams should be ordered and have a key.

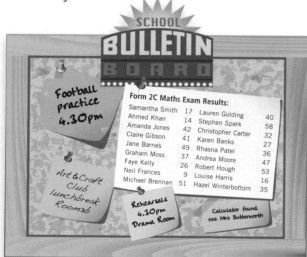

Example

These are some marks gained by students in a Maths exam:

17　14　42　41　49　37　26　9　　51
40　58　32　27　36　47　53　16　35
Key 2|6 represents 26

When the information is put into a stem and leaf diagram it looks like this:

Unordered

Stem	Leaf
0	9
1	7 4 6
2	6 7
3	6 7 2 5
4	2 7 1 0 9
5	1 3 8

Ordered

Stem	Leaf
0	9
1	4 6 7
2	6 7
3	2 5 6 7
4	0 1 2 7 9
5	1 3 8

Quick Test

1. A stem and leaf diagram is a type of plant. True or false?
2. In a questionnaire a question reads: 'For how many hours do you watch TV?'. Write down a better way of asking this question.
3. For $160 \leq h < 170$ the class interval is 10. True or false?
4. What are the three types of correlation?
5. Decide what type of correlation, if any, there is between these variables:
   a) Height and IQ.
   b) Height and shoe size.
   c) Age of car and price.
   d) Cost of petrol and price of food.

KEY WORDS

Make sure you understand these words before moving on!

- Data collection sheet
- Questionnaire
- Census
- Discrete data
- Continuous data
- Class intervals
- Frequency diagram
- Histogram
- Pie chart
- Scatter diagram
- Correlation
- Line of best fit
- Stem and leaf diagram

Skills Practice

1 Charlotte included this question in her questionnaire:

'What type of books do you read?'

Rewrite Charlotte's question so that it is improved.

2 Draw a pie chart of this data:

Favourite ice cream flavour	Vanilla	Strawberry	Chocolate	Mint
Frequency	3	8	6	7

3 Complete the two-way table which shows how some students travel to school:

	Walk	Car	Coach	Total
Boys	5		26	42
Girls		12		
Total	17			85

4 These results show the number of seconds it takes for some adults to complete a puzzle. Draw a stem and leaf diagram of this data.

26, 39, 32, 38, 41, 62, 41, 25, 58, 25, 37, 65, 46, 58, 59, 27

Averages

There are three types of **average** that you can find for a set of data:

- the **mean**
- the **median**
- the **mode**.

Example

During August an ice cream van sold the following number of ice creams each day over a one-week period.

28, 32, 31, 28, 24, 17, 28

Work out the mean, median, mode.

The **mean** is the (sum of a set of values) ÷ (number of values used).

$$\text{Mean} = \frac{(28 + 32 + 31 + 28 + 24 + 17 + 28)}{7}$$
$$= \frac{188}{7}$$

Mean = 26.86 (2 d.p.)

The **mode** in any set of data is the value that occurs the most often. If there are two modes, this is known as bimodal.

Mode = 28 ice creams

The **median** of a set of data is the middle value when the data is put in to order.

28, 32, 31, 28, 24, 17, 28

reordered goes:

17, 24, 28, (28), 28, 31, 32

Median = 28 ice creams sold

Range

The **range** of a set of data tells you how spread out the data is. It is the difference between the highest and lowest values.

Range	=	Highest Value	—	Lowest Value

Example

The range in the number of ice creams sold is:

Range = 32 − 17
       = 15 ice creams

Making Comparisons

The average and range are used to compare two or more sets of data.

Example

During the Olympics, two archery competitors had the following results:

Competitor	Mean score	Range
Australia	9.3	3
France	9.2	1

Each shot carries a maximum of 10 points.

From the results we can see that the Australian competitor had a higher mean score. But, since their range is higher than the French competitor their accuracy is not as consistent.

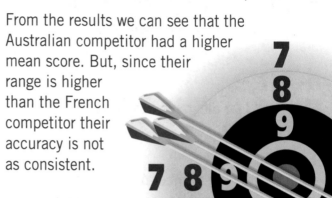

Averages from a Frequency Table

Data is often shown in a **frequency table**. Frequency tables can be used to find the mean, median, mode and range.

Example

The frequency table show the marks for 20 students in a times tables test.

The table shows that...
- 1 student gained 4 marks
- 2 students gained 5 marks, and so on.

$$\text{Mean} = \frac{\text{Total (of frequency} \times \text{number of marks)}}{\text{Total of the frequency}}$$

Mark (x)	Frequency (f)	$x \times f$
4	1	4
5	2	10
6	0	0
7	1	7
8	8	64
9	5	45
10	3	30

$$\frac{(1 \times 4) + (2 \times 5) + (0 \times 6) + (1 \times 7) + (8 \times 8) + (5 \times 9) + (3 \times 10)}{1 + 2 + 0 + 1 + 8 + 5 + 3}$$

$$= \frac{160}{20}$$

$$= 8$$

Median: Since there are 20 students the median must lie between the 10th and 11th mark.

Counting up the frequency table gives the value as 8 marks.

Mode: This is the mark that occurs the most or has the highest frequency.
    = 8 marks.

Range = highest mark – lowest mark
    = 10 – 4
    = 6 marks.

Mark (x)	Frequency (f)
4	1
5	2
6	0
7	1
8	8
9	5
10	3

10th, 11th value in here

Averages

Using Stem and Leaf Diagrams to Find Averages

Stem and leaf diagrams can be used to find averages.

Example
John records the number of text messages he receives each day. Here are the results for the last 15 days.

Stem	Leaf
0	2 2 6
1	3 3 7 7 ⑦ 8 9
2	2 4 5 8
3	1

Key
2|5 represents 25 texts

Range = 31 − 2

     = 29 texts

Median = this is the 8th value. John got 17 texts

Mode = 17 texts, since 17 texts were received on 3 of the days.

Quick Test

1. The mode of these numbers is 1.
   True or false?
   7, 2, 1, 1, 2, 1, 4, 6, 1
2. Explain how you would find the range of a set of data?
3. What is the range of this data?
   7, 9, 11, 4, 1, 7, 2
   A 12   **B** 10   **C** 9   **D** 8

KEY WORDS
Make sure you understand these words before moving on!
• Average
• Mean
• Median
• Mode
• Range
• Frequency table
• Stem and leaf

Skills Practice

1 For this set of data:
7, 9, 4, 1, 5, 5, 5, 6

Find the:
a) Mean　　　　**b)** Median　　　　**c)** Mode　　　　**d)** Range

2 Nigel needs to pick a forward for the football team. He looks at the scoring record for Paulo and Cesc.

In Paulo's last seven matches he has scored 2, 2, 1, 0, 0, 3 and 2 goals.

In Cesc's last seven matches he has scored 3, 2, 2, 1, 1, 1 and 1 goals.

Work out the mean, medium, mode and range for Paulo and Cesc. Who should Nigel choose and why?

3 The number of merits awarded to each student in a class last week is shown in the table below:

Merits (x)	0	1	2	3	4	5
Frequency (f)	2	1	1	12	8	7

Work out:
a) The modal number of merits awarded.
b) The range of the number of merits awarded.
c) The mean number of merits awarded.
d) The median number of merits awarded to students.

4 Eleven swimmers had their times recorded (to the nearest 10th of a second) for the 50m freestyle. Their times are shown in the stem and leaf diagram below:

Use the diagram to find:
a) The range of the times.　　　**b)** The median time.　　　**c)** The modal time.

Stem	Leaf
28	6　7
29	5
30	8　9　9
31	4　4　4　7
32	1

Key
29|5 represents 29.5 seconds

Probability

Probability

Probability is the chance or **likelihood** that something will happen.

An **event** is something that happens. Every event has a set of possible outcomes. In probability, events are considered that have one or more possible **outcomes**. For example, when a coin is thrown the possible outcomes are a head or a tail.

The probability that an event can happen lies between 0 and 1.

The probability scale:
- starts at 0 for something that's impossible.
- finishes at 1 for something that's certain.

0	Even	1
Impossible	chance	Certain

Probabilities can be written as:
- Fractions
- Decimals
- Percentages

Theoretical Probability

The theoretical probability (or probability of an outcome) is calculated in the following way:

$$\text{Probability of an outcome} = \frac{\text{Number of ways an outcome can happen}}{\text{Total number of outcomes}}$$

P (outcome) is the shortened way of writing the probability of an outcome.

Example
A bag contains 6 red, 4 blue and 3 yellow counters. A counter is taken from the bag at random. What is the probability of choosing a...

a) red counter? $\frac{6}{13}$

b) blue counter? $\frac{4}{13}$

c) yellow counter? $\frac{3}{13}$

d) green counter? 0

Experimental Probability

The experimental probability of an outcome can be calculated after an experiment has been completed.

$$\text{Experimental probability} = \frac{\text{Number of times the outcome happened}}{\text{Total number of times experiment carried out}}$$

The experimental probability is the **relative frequency** of the event happening.

Example
Molly threw a coin 100 times to estimate the probability of getting a tail.

Head	Tail
59	41

There are 100 outcomes of which 41 are favourable (i.e. tails).

Experimental Probability: P (tail) = $\frac{41}{100}$ = 0.41

The Theoretical Probability of a tail: P (tail) = $\frac{50}{100}$ = 0.5

Probability of an Event Not Happening

If you know the probability of an event happening you can work out the probability of an event not happening:

| P (Outcome will happen) | = | 1 – P (Outcome will not happen) |

or

| P (Outcome will not happen) | = | 1 – P (Outcome will happen) |

Examples

1. The probability that a train arrives late is $\frac{2}{11}$. What is the probability that a train does not arrive late?

   P (train late) = 1 – P (train on time)

   $$= 1 - \frac{2}{11}$$

   $$= \frac{9}{11}$$

2. The probability that Pradnya gets a grade C in GCSE Maths is 0.81. What is the probability that Pradnya will not get a grade C?

   P (not get a C) = 1 – P (will get a C)

   $$= 1 - 0.81$$

   $$= 0.19$$

Possible Outcomes for Two or More Events

Tests, diagrams and tables can be used when considering outcomes of two or more events.

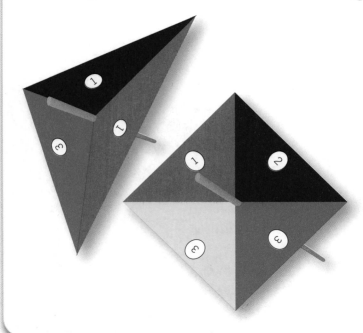

Examples

1. **Sample Space Diagrams**

   Two spinners are spun at the same time, and their scores added. Represent the outcomes on a sample space diagram.

		Spinner 1		
+		1	1	3
	1	2	2	4
Spinner 2	2	3	3	5
	3	4	4	6
	3	4	4	6

   There are 12 outcomes.

   What is:

   a) P (score of 4) = $\frac{5}{12}$

   b) P (odd score) = $\frac{3}{12} = \frac{1}{4}$

   c) P (score of 9) = 0

Probability

Possible Outcomes for Two or More Events (cont.)

2 The diagrams show two spinners. One is coloured and the other is numbered: 4, 5 and 6. Write a list of all possible outcomes:

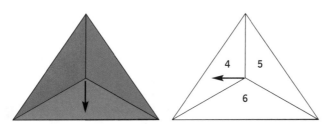

Red 4	Green 4	Blue 4
Red 5	Green 5	Blue 5
Red 6	Green 6	Blue 6

3 The diagram shows a two-way table for pupils in a class who are studying either French or German.

Language	Male	Female	Total
French	6	2	8
German	4	5	9
Total	10	7	17

If a pupil is chosen at random, what is the probability that they are studying German?

P (German) = $\frac{9}{17}$

If a boy is chosen at random, what is the probability he is studying French?

P (French) = $\frac{6}{10}$ ⟵ 6 boys study French
⟵ 10 boys in total

Quick Test

1 What is probability?

2 In a bag there are 6 red and 3 green beads. The probability of choosing a green bead at random is $\frac{6}{9}$. True or false?

3 The probability of being late is $\frac{7}{9}$. What is the probability of not being late?

4 The probability of getting 4 on a fair die is $\frac{1}{6}$. True or false?

KEY WORDS

Make sure you understand these words before moving on!
- Probability
- Likelihood
- Event
- Outcome
- Relative frequency
- Sample space diagrams

1. A drawer has 3 red, 4 black and 2 grey socks. A sock is taken out of the drawer at random.

   What is the probability of choosing:
   a) A red sock?
   b) A black sock?
   c) A grey sock?
   d) A blue sock?

2. The probability that it will snow on any day in December is 23%. Work out the probability that it will not snow on any day in December.

3. The probability of winning the premium bonds is 0.1
   What is the probability of not winning the premium bonds?

4. The probability that a traffic light is red is $\frac{2}{5}$. What is the probability that it isn't red?

5. During the options process you can choose one subject from each option block.

Option 1	Option 2
Geography	History
French	German
Technology	ICT

   Write down all the possible outcomes.

6. Two dice are thrown and their scores are added.
   Copy and complete the sample space diagram.

   What is the probability of a score of:
   a) 3
   b) 7
   c) 12
   d) 15

   Dice 2

+	1	2	3	4	5	6
1	2	3	4	5	6	7
2	3	4	5	6	7	8
3	4	5	6	7	8	9
4	5	6				
5	6	7				
6	7	8				12

   Dice 1

Index